Teaching Resources
UNIT 2

California *Focus on* **Physical Science**

PEARSON

Prentice Hall

Boston, Massachusetts
Upper Saddle River, New Jersey

ISBN 0-13-203475-1

1 2 3 4 5 6 7 8 9 10   09 08 07 06 05

Unit 2 Chemical Building Blocks

CALIFORNIA

Your Keys to Success

Read for Meaning

This textbook has been developed to fully support your understanding of the science concepts in the California Science Standards. Each chapter contains built-in reading support.

Before You Read

Use the Standards Focus to preview the California Science Standards that are covered, the key concepts, and key terms in the section.

Standards Focus
The California Science Standards that you will learn are listed at the beginning of each section.

Key Concepts
Each science standard is broken down into smaller ideas called Key Concepts.

Key Terms Use the list of key terms to preview the vocabulary for each section.

Section

1

What Is Physical Science

CALIFORNIA
Standards Focus

S 8.9 Scientific progress is made by asking meaningful questions and conducting careful investigations.

- What skills do scientists use to learn about the world?
- What do physical scientists study?

Key Terms
- science
- observing
- inferring
- predicting
- chemistry
- physics

Lab zone Standards **Warm-Up**

How Does a Ball Bounce?
1. Your teacher will give you three balls and a meter sti the meter stick with the zero end touching the floor.
2. Hold one ball beside the top of the meter stick so it c touch. Drop the ball. Have a partner record the heigh first bounce.
3. Repeat Step 2 twice using the same ball.
4. Repeat Steps 2 and 3 for each of the other balls.

Think It Over
Predicting Can you use your data to predict accurately h ball will bounce in the future? Explain.

As you walk around an amusement park, you may wo the rides work. How does a ferris wheel spin? Ho bumper cars work? What makes the neon lights so Why don't people fall out of the roller coaster as it co loop? These are all questions that physical science ca answer. The designers of amusement parks must kne deal about physical science to make sure that visito ence fun and thrills while staying safe.

An amusement park is a ▶ great place to observe physical science in action.

s You Read

y Concepts in boldface
ntences allow you to
cus on the important ideas
the chapter.

> Look for the green
> and yellow keys to
> find the key concepts
> in each section.

Skills Scientists Use

Science is the study of the natural world. Science includes all of the knowledge gained by exploring nature. To think and work like a scientist, you need to use the same skills that they do. 🔑 **Scientists use the skills of observing, inferring, and predicting to learn more about the natural world.**

Observing Scientists observe things. **Observing** means using one or more senses to gather information. Your senses include sight, hearing, touch, taste, and smell. Each day of your life, you observe things that help you decide what to eat, what to wear, and whether to stay inside or go out.

Scientists usually make observations in a careful, orderly way. They make both qualitative and quantitative observations. Qualitative observations are descriptions that don't involve numbers or measurements. Noticing that a ball is round, that milk smells sour, or that a car is moving is a qualitative observation. Quantitative observations are measurements. You make a quantitative observation when you measure your height or weight. In science, observations may also be called evidence, or data.

Inferring When you explain your observations, you are **inferring**, or making an inference. Inferences are based on reasoning from what you already know. You make inferences all the time without thinking about it. For example, your teacher gives lots of surprise quizzes. So if your teacher walks into the room carrying a stack of paper, you may infer that the pages contain a quiz. But inferences are not always correct. The papers could be announcements to be taken home.

Predicting Every day, people make statements about the future. **Predicting** means making a forecast of what ... on past experience or ... cientists predict the ... and current infor- ... t is based on data, ... ss.

... s based on?

Go Online
PHSchool.com

For: More on scientific thinking
Visit: PHSchool.com
Web Code: cgd-6011

FIGURE 1 Inferring
When you explain or interpret your observations, you are making an inference. *Inferring* How do you think these young women obtained the stuffed bear? Explain your reasoning.

Temperature

As you head out the door each morning, one of the first things you might notice is the temperature. Is it cold out this morning? How high will the temperature rise?

Units of Temperature Scientists commonly use the Celsius temperature scale. On the **Celsius Scale**, water freezes at 0°C and boils at 100°C. There are exactly 100 degrees between the freezing point and boiling point of water. Normal human body temperature is about 37°C.

In addition to the Celsius scale, scientists also use another temperature scale, called the **Kelvin scale**. Units on the Kelvin scale are the same size as those on the Celsius scale. 🔑 **The kelvin (K) is the SI unit of temperature.**

The temperature 0 K on the Kelvin scale is called **absolute zero.** Nothing can get colder than this temperature. Absolute zero is equal to −273°C on the Celsius scale.

Measuring Temperature You can measure temperature using a thermometer. Most thermometers consist of a sealed tube that contains a liquid. The liquid expands or contracts as the temperature changes.

Celsius (°C)	Kelvin (K)	
Boiling Point of Water	100	373
Freezing Point of Water	0	273
Absolute Zero	−273	0

FIGURE 16
Measuring Temperature
Scientists use the Celsius and Kelvin scales to measure temperature.

After You Read

The Section Assessment tests your understanding of the Key Concepts. Each bank of Reviewing Key Concept questions here focuses on one of the Key Concepts.

> If you can't answer these items, go back and review the section.

Section 3 Assessment

S 8.8.a, 8.8.b, **E-LA:** Reading 8.2.0, **Math:** 7NS1.2

🎯 **Target Reading Skill** Preview Text Structure Complete the graphic organizer for this section. What question did you ask about Weight and Mass? What was your answer?

🔑 **Reviewing Key Concepts**

1. **a. Identifying** What is the standard measurement system used by scientists around the world?
   b. Predicting Suppose that two scientists use different measurement systems in their work. What problems might arise if they shared their data?
2. **a. Listing** What are the SI units of length, mass, volume, density, time, and temperature?

   b. Estimating Estimate the length of a baseball bat and mass of a baseball in SI units. How can you check how close your estimates are?
   c. Describing Outline a step-by-step method for determining the density of a baseball.

Math Practice

Two solid cubes have the same mass. They each have a mass of 50 g.

3. **Calculating Density** Cube A has a volume of 2 cm × 2 cm × 2 cm. What is its density?
4. **Calculating Density** Cube B has a volume of 4 cm × 4 cm × 4 cm. What is its density?

Your Keys to Success

How to Read Science

 The target reading skills introduced on this page will help you read and understand information in this textbook. Each chapter introduces a reading Developing these reading skills is key to becomin successful reader in science and other subject are.

Preview Text Structure By understanding how textbooks are organized, you can gain information from them more effectively. This textbook is organized with red headings and blue subheadings. Before you read, preview the headings. Ask yourself questions to guide you as you read. **(Chapter 1)**

Preview Visuals The visuals in your science textbook provide important information. Visuals are photographs, graphs, tables, diagrams, and illustrations. Before you read, take the time to preview the visuals in a section. Look closely at the title, labels, and captions. Then ask yourself questions about the visuals. **(Chapter 4)**

Sequence Many parts of a science textbook are organized by sequence. Sequence is the order in which a series of events occurs. Some sections may discuss events in a process that has a beginning and an end. Other sections may describe a continuous process that does not have an end. **(Chapters 11 and 12)**

Compare and Contrast Science texts often make comparisons. When you compare and contrast, you examine the similarities and differences between things. You can compare and contrast by using a table or a Venn diagram. **(Chapters 5 and 8)**

Analyze Cause and Effect A cause makes something happen. An effect is what happens. When you recognize that one event causes another, you are relating cause and effect. **(Chapter 13)**

Identify Main Ideas As you read, you can understand a section or paragraph more clearly by finding the main idea. The main idea the most important idea. The details in a sectio or paragraph support the main idea. Headings and subheadings can often help you identify the main ideas. **(Chapters 2 and 9)**

Identify Supporting Evidence Science textbooks often describe the scientific evidence that supports a theory or hypothesis. Scientific evidence includes data and facts, information whose accuracy can be confirmed by experimen or observation. A hypothesis is a possible explanation for observations made by scientists or an answer to a scientific question. **(Chapter 1**

Create Outlines You can create outlines to help you clarify the text. An outline shows the relationship between main ideas and supporting details. Use the text structure—headings, subheadings, key concepts, and key terms— to help you figure out information to include in your outline. **(Chapters 3, 7, and 14)**

Take Notes Science chapters are packed with information. Taking good notes is one way to he you remember key ideas and to see the big picture. When you take notes, include key ideas, a few details, and summaries. **(Chapters 6 and 10)**

⊙ Target Reading Skills

ch chapter provides a target reading skill with clear
struction to help you read and understand the text.
u will apply the skill as you read. Then you will record
hat you've learned in the section and chapter assessments.

Before You Read
Each chapter introduces a target reading skill and provides examples and practice exercises.

As You Read
As you read, you can use the target reading skill to help you increase your understanding.

After You Read
You can apply the target reading skill in the Section Assessments and in the Chapter Assessments.

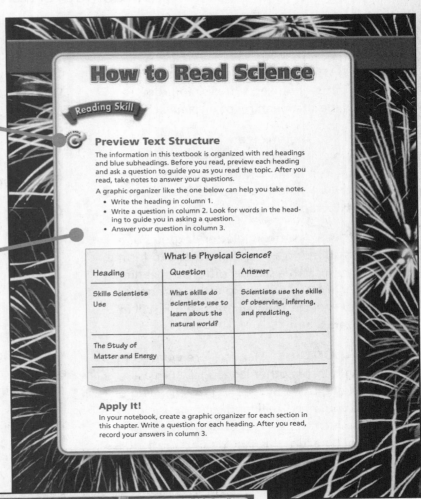

How to Read Science

Reading Skill

Preview Text Structure

The information in this textbook is organized with red headings and blue subheadings. Before you read, preview each heading and ask a question to guide you as you read the topic. After you read, take notes to answer your questions.

A graphic organizer like the one below can help you take notes.
- Write the heading in column 1.
- Write a question in column 2. Look for words in the heading to guide you in asking a question.
- Answer your question in column 3.

What Is Physical Science?

Heading	Question	Answer
Skills Scientists Use	What skills do scientists use to learn about the natural world?	Scientists use the skills of observing, inferring, and predicting.
The Study of Matter and Energy		

Apply It!
In your notebook, create a graphic organizer for each section in this chapter. Write a question for each heading. After you read, record your answers in column 3.

Section 3 Assessment

S 8.8.a, 8.8.b, **E-LA:** Reading 8.2.0, **Math:** 7NS1.2

⊙ **Target Reading Skill** Preview Text Structure
Complete the graphic organizer for this section. What question did you ask about Weight and Mass? What was your answer?

Reviewing Key Concepts
1. a. **Identifying** What is the standard measurement system used by scientists around the world?
   b. **Predicting** Suppose that two scientists use different measurement systems in their work. What problems might arise if they shared their data?
2. a. **Listing** What are the SI units of length, mass, volume, density, time, and temperature?

b. **Estimating** Estimate the length of a baseball bat and mass of a baseball in SI units. How can you check how close your estimates are?
c. **Describing** Outline a step-by-step method for determining the density of a baseball.

Math Practice

Two solid cubes have the same mass. They each have a mass of 50 g.

3. **Calculating Density** Cube A has a volume of 2 cm × 2 cm × 2 cm. What is its density?
4. **Calculating Density** Cube B has a volume of 4 cm × 4 cm × 4 cm. What is its density?

Your Keys to Success

Build Science Vocabulary

 Studying science involves learning a new vocabulary. Here are some vocabulary skills to help you learn the meaning of words you do not recognize.

Word Analysis
You can use your knowledge of word parts—prefixes, suffixes, and roots—to determine the meaning of unfamiliar words.

Prefixes A prefix is a word part that is added at the beginning of a root or base word to change its meaning. Knowing the meaning of prefixes will help you figure out new words. You will practice this skill in Chapter 2.

Suffixes A suffix is a letter or group of letters added to the end of a word to form a new word with a slightly different meaning. Adding a suffix to a word often changes its part of speech. You will practice this skill in Chapters 3 and 15.

Word Origins Many science words come to English from other languages, such as Greek and Latin. By learning the meaning of a few common Greek and Latin roots, you can determine the meaning of new science words. You will practice this skill in Chapters 4, 10, 12, and 14.

Use Clues to Determine Meaning
When you come across a word you don't recognize in science texts, you can use context clues to figure out what the word means. First look for clues in the word itself. Then look at the surrounding words, sentences, and paragraphs for clues. You will practice this skill in Chapter 8.

Identify Multiple Meanings
To understand science concepts, you must use terms precisely. Some familiar words may have different meanings in science. Watch for these multiple-meaning words as you read. You will practice this skill in Chapters 6 and 11.

Identify Related Word Forms
You can increase your vocabulary by learning related forms of words or word families. If you know the meaning of a verb form, you may be able to figure out the related noun and adjective forms. You will practice this skill in Chapter 7.

atmos + sphaira = atmosphere
vapor   sphere   a layer of
gas   vapor or
                       gases that
                       surrounds
                       Earth

Vocabulary Skills

One of the important steps in reading this science textbook is to be sure that you understand the Key Terms. Your book shows several strategies to help learn important vocabulary.

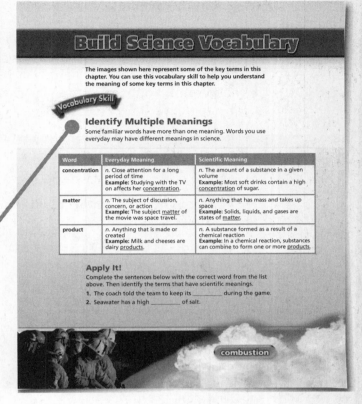

Build Science Vocabulary

The images shown here represent some of the key terms in this chapter. You can use this vocabulary skill to help you understand the meaning of some key terms in this section.

Vocabulary Skill

Identify Multiple Meanings
Some familiar words have more than one meaning. Words you use everyday may have different meanings in science.

Word	Everyday Meaning	Scientific Meaning
concentration	n. Close attention for a long period of time **Example:** Studying with the TV on affects her concentration.	n. The amount of a substance in a given volume **Example:** Most soft drinks contain a high concentration of sugar.
matter	n. The subject of discussion, concern, or action **Example:** The subject matter of the movie was space travel.	n. Anything that has mass and takes up space **Example:** Solids, liquids, and gases are states of matter.
product	n. Anything that is made or created **Example:** Milk and cheeses are dairy products.	n. A substance formed as a result of a chemical reaction **Example:** In a chemical reaction, substances can combine to form one or more products.

Apply It!
Complete the sentences below with the correct word from the list above. Then identify the terms that have scientific meanings.
1. The coach told the team to keep its _____ during the game.
2. Seawater has a high _____ of salt.

combustion

Before You Read
Each chapter introduces a Vocabulary Skill with examples and practice exercises. Key Terms come alive through visuals. The beginning of each section lists the Key Terms.

Carbon-12
6 Neutrons

Carbon-13
7 Neutrons

Carbon-14
8 Neutrons

FIGURE 10
Isotopes
Atoms of all isotopes of carbon contain 6 protons and 6 electrons, but they differ in their number of neutrons. Carbon-12 is the most common isotope.
Interpreting Diagrams Which isotope of carbon has the largest mass number?

Isotopes and Mass Number Although the number of protons is fixed for a particular element, the same is not true for the number of neutrons in the nucleus. Atoms of the same element that have different numbers of neutrons are called **isotopes** (EYE suh tohps). Three carbon isotopes are illustrated in Figure 10. Each carbon atom has 6 protons and 6 electrons. But the number of neutrons is 6, 7, or 8. An isotope is identified by its **mass number**, which is the sum of the protons and neutrons in the nucleus of an atom. The most common isotope of carbon has a mass number of 12 (6 protons + 6 neutrons), and may be written as "carbon-12." Two other isotopes are carbon-13 and carbon-14. Despite their different mass numbers, all three carbon isotopes react the same way chemically.

Hydrogen also has three isotopes. All hydrogen atoms have one proton in the nucleus. The most common isotope is hydrogen-1 (1 proton + 0 neutrons). The others are hydrogen-2 (1 proton + 1 neutron) and hydrogen-3 (1 proton + 2 neutrons). Hydrogen-2 is called deuterium. Hydrogen-3 is called tritium.

As You Read
Each Key Term is highlighted in yellow, appears in boldfaced type, and is followed by a definition.

Section 1 Assessment
S 8.3.a, 8.7.b,
E-LA: Reading 8.1.2

Vocabulary Skill Greek Word Origins Use what you know about the Greek word *atomos* to explain the meaning of *atom*.

Reviewing Key Concepts
1. a. Reviewing Why did atomic theory change with time?
   b. Describing Describe Bohr's model of the atom. What specific information did Bohr contribute to scientists' understanding of the atom?
   c. Comparing and Contrasting How is the modern atomic model different from Bohr's model?
2. a. Reviewing What are the three main particles in the modern model of an atom?

   b. Explaining What is atomic number? How is it used to distinguish one element from another?
   c. Applying Concepts The atomic number of nitrogen is 7. How many protons, neutrons, and electrons make up an atom of nitrogen-15?

Lab zone At-Home **Activity**

Modeling Atoms Build a three-dimensional model of an atom using materials such as beads, cotton, and clay. Show the model to your family, and explain what makes atoms of different elements different from one another.

After You Read
You can practice the Vocabulary Skill in the Section Assessments. You can apply your understanding of the Key Terms in the Chapter Assessments.

130 ◆

Letter Home

Dear Family Member:

As your child's science teacher, I am looking forward to helping your child learn about physical science. Research has shown that family involvement plays a significant role in student performance. Because I know that you want your child to be successful, I offer these suggestions so that you can help your child gain proficiency in science.

- ✔ Ask your child about homework assignments and check that he or she has completed each assignment.
- ✔ Provide a quiet place and regular time for your child to do homework.
- ✔ Help your child collect materials and information for school activities and projects.
- ✔ Read. Your child looks to you as a model. If you read often about science, he or she will value the activity.
- ✔ Encourage computer literacy. Advise your child to use computers in school or at the library. If you have a home computer, help your child do research online.

In this unit, your child will learn that chemical reactions are processes in which atoms are rearranged into different combinations of molecules. The unit will also investigate the characteristics of acids and bases. In addition, your child will find out that carbon, because it can combine in many ways with itself and other elements, has a key role in the chemistry of living organisms.

As you may know, the state of California has established standards describing the science knowledge and skills for which students are responsible. State assessments of student learning will be based on the content and skills described in these standards. Your child will be using a textbook entitled *Science Explorer: Focus on Physical Science*, published by Pearson Prentice Hall. The textbook aligns with the portion of the California content standards that covers life science and on which your child will be assessed.

I encourage you to stay involved throughout the school year. Visit the classroom during open house or make an appointment with me if you have questions. Show that you value science education and all of your child's efforts toward success in school.

Cordially,

_____

Science Teacher

Estimado familiar:

Como profesor de ciencias de su niño o niña, quiero ayudarle a aprender más acerca de las Ciencias de la Física. Algunos estudios han demostrado que la ayuda familiar juega un papel fundamental en el rendimiento del estudiante. Como sé que usted quiere que su niño o niña tenga éxito, le hago las siguientes sugerencias para que pueda ayudarle a mejorar en ciencias.

✔ Pregunte a su niño o niña por sus tareas y revise que haya terminado cada una de ellas.

✔ Dé a su niño o niña un lugar tranquilo y una hora fija para que pueda hacer sus tareas.

✔ Ayude a su niño o niña a obtener materiales e información para las actividades y proyectos escolares.

✔ Lea. Su niño o niña le ve a usted como su modelo. Si usted lee a menudo sobre ciencias, él o ella dará importancia a esa actividad.

✔ Anímele a conocer mejor la computadora. Aconseje a su niño o niña que use las computadoras en la escuela o la biblioteca. Si tiene computadora en casa, ayude a su niño o niña a hacer sus investigaciones en línea.

En esta unidad, su niño o niña estudiará que las reacciones químicas son procesos en los cuales los átomos se reordenan en diferentes combinaciones moleculares. La unidad también investigará las características de los ácidos y las bases. Además, su niño o niña descubrirá que el carbón, al poder combinarse de muchas maneras consigo mismo y con otros elementos, tiene un papel importante en la química de los organismos vivos.

Como quizá ya sepa, el estado de California ha establecido una normativa que describe el conocimiento y destrezas sobre la ciencia que deben conocer los estudiantes. La evaluación estatal del aprendizaje del estudiante estará basada en el contenido y las destrezas descritas en esta normativa. Su niño o niña usará un libro titulado *Explorador de ciencias: Enfoque en las Ciencias físicas*, publicado por Pearson Prentice Hall. El libro de texto contempla la porción de la normativa de contenido de California que cubre las Ciencias de la Física por la que su niño o niña será evaluado.

Le animo a que ayude a su estudiante durante todo el año escolar. Visite su clase en los días señalados o comuníquese conmigo si tiene alguna pregunta. Demuestre que usted valora la educación científica y todos los esfuerzos de su niño o niña para que tenga éxito en la escuela.

Atentamente,

_____

Profesor de ciencias

Chapter 5 Atoms and Bonding

Atoms, Bonding, and the Periodic Table

⏱ *2 3/4 periods, 1 block*

Objectives
5.1.1 Explain how the reactivity of elements is related to valence electrons in atoms.
5.1.2 State what the periodic table tells you about atoms and the properties of elements.

🜨 California Standards
❑ S 8.3.f

PRETEACH

Build Background Knowledge
Students use a familiar analogy to understand why it is important for elements to be organized.

 **Standards Warm-Up** *What Are the Trends in the Periodic Table?* **L2**

Resources
❑ **Vocabulary Flashcards**
  L2 Chapter 5 Vocabulary
❑ **Build Science Vocabulary** *Online*
  L2 Chapter 5 Vocabulary

INSTRUCT

Valence Electrons and Bonding Introduce electron dot diagrams to help students visualize valence electrons and understand their role in bonding.
How the Periodic Table Works Guide students in learning how to use the periodic table by asking them to locate information in the periodic table.

 Skills Lab *Comparing Atom Sizes* **L2**

Resources
❑ **Reading/Notetaking Guides**
  (Adapted versions available)
  Chapter 5, Section 1
❑ **Color Transparencies Book**
  L2 PS45, PS46
❑ **Laboratory Manual**
  L2 *Comparing Atom Sizes*
  Student Worksheets
❑ **Lab Activity DVD Library**
  L2 Skills Lab: *Comparing Atom Sizes*
❑ **Student Edition in MP3 Format**
❑ **Spanish Section Summaries in MP3 Forma**
❑ **www.SciLinks.org** Web Code: cgp–1032

ASSESS/REMEDIATE

Assess Progress
Evaluate student comprehension with the Section Assessment and Section Quiz.
Remediation
Students identify properties of different types of elements, including noble gases, halogens and alkali metals.

Resources
❑ **Teaching Resources, Unit 2**
  L2 Section 5.1 Quiz
  L1 5.1 Review and Reinforce, ELL, LPR, SN
  L3 5.1 Enrich, AR, GT

Atoms, Bonding, and the Periodic Table

Understanding Main Ideas

Use the diagrams to answer questions 1–5 in the spaces provided.

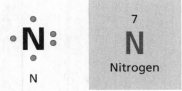

1. What is the atomic number of the element represented by the diagrams?
   _____

2. How many protons does the element have? _____

3. How many valence electrons does the element have? _____

4. Is the element reactive or stable? How do you know?
   _____
   _____

5. Is the element a metal or nonmetal? _____

6. What are valence electrons?
   _____
   _____

7. The force of attraction that holds two atoms together is called a(n)
   _____

8. Name two events involving electrons that can result in the formation of chemical bonds between atoms.
   _____
   _____

9. How can you tell whether or not an element will react with other elements?
   _____
   _____

10. What do atoms of elements in the same group of the periodic table have in common?
    _____

11. When metals react with other elements, the atoms of the metals
    _____ electrons.

12. When nonmetals react with metals, the atoms of the nonmetals
    _____. When nonmetals react with other
    nonmetals, the atoms of the nonmetals _____
    electrons.

Atoms and Bonding ▪ *Enrich*

The Rockets' Red Glare

Many people enjoy fireworks displays on the Fourth of July. Did you know that chemistry plays a big part in the beauty and the noise? Depending on the chemical compounds used in each firework rocket, different colors and effects are produced. A diagram of a typical rocket is shown at the right. When the gunpowder at the bottom of the rocket is lit, it lifts the rocket off the ground and into the air. When the rocket reaches its maximum height, a second fuse burns, setting the other chemicals in the rocket on fire. As these chemicals burn, they produce smoke, color bursts, loud noises, or a combination of these things.

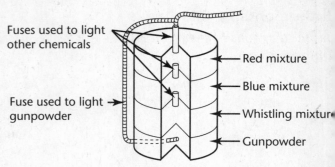

The table below lists some chemicals and the effects they produce when combined in a rocket.

Element	Effect
strontium	red color
barium	green color
copper	blue color
sodium	yellow color
magnesium or aluminum	white color
potassium or sodium	whistling sound
potassium and sulfur	white smoke

Answer the following questions on a separate sheet of paper.

1. What groups of the periodic table do the majority of the elements listed in the table above belong to? Why do you think elements in these groups are used in making fireworks?

2. What group of elements could you NOT use in making fireworks? Explain your answer.

3. Why would you want to have two or more separate fuses in a rocket?

4. Solutions of magnesium, barium, and strontium are clear and colorless. Predict what might happen if a drop of each solution was held in the flame of a lab burner.

Ionic Bonds

ABILITY LEVELS KEY
L1 Basic to Average
L2 For All Students
L3 Average to Advanced

4 periods, 2 blocks

Atoms and Bonding

Objectives

5.2.1 Explain how ions form bonds.
5.2.2 Explain how the formulas and names of ionic compounds are written.
5.2.3 Identify the properties of ionic compounds.

California Standards
☐ S 8.3.b
☐ S 8.3.c

PRETEACH

Build Background Knowledge
Students recall what they have learned about electrons and electrical charge as a review of what they need to know to understand ions and ionic bonds.

Lab zone Standards Warm-Up *How Do Ions Form?* L2

Resources
☐ **Vocabulary Flashcards**
    L2 Chapter 5 Vocabulary
☐ **Build Science Vocabulary** *Online*
    L2 Chapter 5 Vocabulary

INSTRUCT

Ions Introduce common ions that students will see throughout the book.
Chemical Formulas and Names Explain how chemical formulas reflect the composition of ionic compounds.
Properties of Ionic Compounds Have students compare and contrast different ionic compounds to infer their shared properties.

Lab zone Skills Lab *Shedding Light on Ions* L2

Resources
☐ **Reading/Notetaking Guides**
    (Adapted versions available)
    Chapter 5, Section 2
☐ **Color Transparencies Book**
    L2 PS48, PS49
☐ **Laboratory Manual**
    L2 *Shedding Light on Ions*
    Student Worksheets
☐ **Lab Activity DVD Library**
    L2 Skills Lab: *Shedding Light on Ions*
☐ **Student Edition in MP3 Format**
☐ **Spanish Section Summaries in MP3 Format**
☐ **www.SciLinks.org** Web Code: scn-1213

ASSESS/REMEDIATE

Assess Progress
Evaluate student comprehension with the Section Assessment and Section Quiz.

Remediation
Students describe properties of ionic compounds.

Resources
☐ **Teaching Resources, Unit 2**
    L2 Section 5.2 Quiz
    L1 5.2 Review and Reinforce, ELL, LPR, SN
    L3 5.2 Enrich, AR, GT

Atoms and Bonding · *Review and Reinforce*

Ionic Bonds

Understanding Main Ideas

Answer the following questions on a separate sheet of paper.

1. How does an atom become a positive ion? How does an atom become a negative ion?
2. How do ions form electrically neutral compounds?
3. What characteristics do solid ionic compounds share?
4. Why does the electrical conductivity of ionic compounds change when they are dissolved in water?

Ions and Their Charges		
Name	**Charge**	**Symbol/Formula**
Ammonium	1+	NH_4^+
Potassium	1+	K^+
Calcium	2+	Ca^{2+}
Magnesium	2+	Mg^{2+}
Chloride	1–	Cl^-
Oxide	2–	O^{2-}
Sulfide	2–	S^{2-}
Phosphate	3–	PO_4^{3-}

Use the chart above to answer the following on a separate sheet of paper.

5. How many potassium ions are needed to balance the charge of one sulfide ion? Explain.
6. Predict the formulas for calcium chloride and potassium phosphate.
7. Name the following compounds: MgS, NH_4Cl, and K_2O.
8. Which ions in the table are polyatomic ions?

Building Vocabulary

Answer the following questions on a separate sheet of paper.

9. What is an ion?
10. What is an ionic bond?
11. What is the arrangement of ions in a crystal?

Atoms and Bonding ▪ *Enrich*

Pulling Away Electrons

You know that the metals in Groups 1 and 2 are quite reactive. They combine easily with certain other elements to form compounds. Atoms from Group 1 react by losing one electron; atoms from Group 2 lose two electrons. It takes energy to remove an electron from an atom. Some atoms hold their electrons tighter than other atoms do. Also, an individual atom holds some of its electrons tighter than other electrons.

The size of an atom's radius affects how tightly it holds its electrons. The larger the radius of an atom, the farther away from the nucleus some of its electrons are. The electron held the least tightly is easiest to remove. To remove yet another electron requires more energy than was needed to remove the first. The figure below compares the atomic radii of the Groups 1 and 2 elements. The number underneath each element represents the atomic radius measured in picometers (pm).

Answer the following questions on a separate sheet of paper.

1. What do you notice about atomic radius as you look down a group? As you look across a period from Group 1 to Group 2?

2. Which element would you expect to be the most reactive in Group 1? In Group 2? Explain your answer.

3. Within each period, which element of the two elements would you expect to be more reactive? Explain your answer.

4. Across the periodic table, atomic radius continues to decrease through Group 17. How does this fact help explain why the metals in Groups 3 through 13 are less reactive than the metals in Groups 1 and 2?

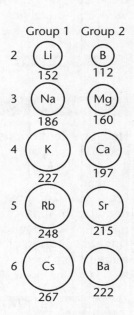

Covalent Bonds

🕐 *1 period, 1/3 block*

Objectives

5.3.1 State what holds covalently bonded atoms together.
5.3.2 Identify the properties of molecular compounds.
5.3.3 Explain how unequal sharing of electrons occurs and how it affects molecules.

🌐 California Standards
☐ S 8.3.b
☐ S 8.7.c

PRETEACH

Build Background Knowledge
Students recall that atoms can form bonds by sharing electrons.

 **Standards Warm-Up** *Can Water and Oil Mix?* **L2**

Resources
☐ **Vocabulary Flashcards**
   L2 Chapter 5 Vocabulary
☐ **Build Science Vocabulary** *Online*
   L2 Chapter 5 Vocabulary

INSTRUCT

How Covalent Bonds Form Introduce covalent bonds by comparing and contrasting them with ionic bonds, with which students are already familiar.
Molecular Compounds Use a graphic organizer to summarize important points about molecular compounds and their properties.
Unequal Sharing of Electrons Use the familiar example of water to explain why some molecules are polar.

Resources
☐ **Reading/Notetaking Guides**
   (Adapted versions available)
   Chapter 5, Section 3
☐ **Color Transparencies Book**
   L2 PS51, PS52, PS53
☐ **Student Edition in MP3 Format**
☐ **Spanish Section Summaries in MP3 Forma**
☐ **www.SciLinks.org** Web Code: scn-1214

ASSESS/REMEDIATE

Assess Progress
Evaluate student comprehension with the Section Assessment and Section Quiz.

Remediation
Students define or describe and give examples of the key terms.

Resources
☐ **Teaching Resources, Unit 2**
   L2 Section 5.3 Quiz
   L1 5.3 Review and Reinforce, ELL, LPR, SN
   L3 5.3 Enrich, AR, GT

Atoms and Bonding · *Review and Reinforce*

Covalent Bonds

Understanding Main Ideas

Answer the following questions in the spaces provided.

(+) H:F: (−)   :O::O:

:N⋮N: :F:F:

1. Circle all the covalent bonds in the electron dot diagrams.

2. Which bond(s) shown are double bonds?

_____

3. Which bond(s) shown are triple bonds?

_____

4. Which molecule(s) shown have nonpolar bonds?

_____

5. What makes the bond in HF a polar bond?

_____

_____

_____

6. How do the melting points, boiling points, and conductivity of molecular compounds compare to those of ionic compounds?

_____

_____

_____

Building Vocabulary

From the list below, choose the term that best completes each sentence. Each term may be used more than once.

nonpolar

polar

7. A covalent bond is considered _____ if the two atoms share the electrons equally.

8. A water molecule is a(n) _____ molecule because the oxygen atom pulls electrons closer to it than the hydrogen atoms do, forming a molecule that is slightly more positive at one end than at the other.

9. A covalent bond is considered _____ if the electrons are shared unequally.

10. A carbon dioxide molecule is a(n) _____ molecule because the oxygen atoms are pulling on the shared electrons with equal strength in opposite directions and cancel each other out.

Atoms and Bonding ▪ *Enrich*

Oil Spills

Each year over 907,000 metric tons of crude oil are spilled in Earth's oceans. This is enough oil to fill 100 school gymnasiums! It is important to clean up crude oil as soon after a spill as possible, because spilled crude oil has negative effects on the environment. Oil on ocean surfaces is harmful to ocean life because it blocks sunlight and reduces the level of dissolved oxygen in the water. In addition, many birds and fish die from contact with crude oil because the oil damages feathers and gills.

Two methods used to clean up oil spills are

1. A floating barrier is placed around the spill to keep it from spreading. Because oil floats on water, the oil can be skimmed off the top of the water. Skimming the top of the water using a net with extremely small holes allows the water to escape but not the oil.

**Figure 1
Detergent Molecule**

Nonpolar end   Polar end

2. Chemicals that act like detergents are sprayed onto the surface of the spill. These chemicals break up the oil into tiny droplets. The small particles of oil spread over a large area have less effect on marine life than larger particles.

**Figure 2
Formation of Oil Droplets**

Polar end of detergent (attracts water)

Water molecule

Oil molecules

Nonpolar end of detergent (attracts oil)

Both of these methods work because of the chemical properties of oil molecules. Oil molecules are nonpolar, so they will not mix with polar water molecules. Detergents are long molecules that have a polar end and a nonpolar end, like the molecule shown in Figure 1. The polar end of the detergent attracts water molecules, and the nonpolar end attracts oil molecules. Figure 2 shows how detergent molecules cause the formation of droplets of water, detergent, and oil molecules.

Answer the following questions on a separate sheet of paper.

1. Explain how the nonpolar character of oil molecules helps when removing oil from water using nets and floating barriers.
2. The long "tail" on a detergent molecule is made up mostly of carbon atoms bonded to other carbon atoms. Why would you expect the tail to be nonpolar?
3. How does detergent sprayed on an oil spill break up the spill?
4. The action of waves can break up large sections of an oil spill. The oil looks like it has mixed with the water, but has it? Explain your answer.

Bonding in Metals

⏱ *1 period, 1/2 block*

ABILITY LEVELS KEY
- **L1** Basic to Average
- **L2** For All Students
- **L3** Average to Advanced

Objectives

5.4.1 Explain how the properties of metals and alloys compare.

5.4.2 Describe how metal atoms are bonded in solid metal.

5.4.3 Explain how metallic bonding results in useful properties of metals.

🌐 California Standards
- ❏ S 8.7.c

PRETEACH

Build Background Knowledge
Students name common objects containing metal and infer properties of metals based on the objects.

Lab zone Standards Warm-Up *Are They "Steel" the Same?* **L1**

Resources
- ❏ **Vocabulary Flashcards**
  - **L2** Chapter 5 Vocabulary
- ❏ **Build Science Vocabulary** *Online*
  - **L2** Chapter 5 Vocabulary

INSTRUCT

Metals and Alloys Explain the difference between metals that are pure elements and "metals" that are alloys with metallic properties.

Metallic Bonding Use the figure in the textbook that shows metallic bonding to help students understand the nature of metallic bonds.

Metallic Properties Explain how the properties of metals depend on the nature of metallic bonds.

Resources
- ❏ **Reading/Notetaking Guides**
  (Adapted versions available)
  Chapter 5, Section 4
- ❏ **Color Transparencies Book**
  - **L2** PS55
- ❏ **Student Edition in MP3 Format**
- ❏ **Spanish Section Summaries in MP3 Format**
- ❏ **www.SciLinks.org** Web Code: scn-1215

ASSESS/REMEDIATE

Assess Progress
Evaluate student comprehension with the Section Assessment and Section Quiz.

Remediation
Students answer questions based on the boldface sentences in the section.

Resources
- ❏ **Teaching Resources, Unit 2**
  - **L2** Section 5.4 Quiz
  - **L1** 5.4 Review and Reinforce, ELL, LPR, SN
  - **L3** 5.4 Enrich, AR, GT

Name _____ Date _____ Class _____

Atoms and Bonding · *Review and Reinforce*

Bonding in Metals

Understanding Main Ideas

Answer questions 1–4 in the spaces provided.

1. What are the properties of metals?

   _____

   _____

2. What is an alloy?

   _____

   _____

3. What does the phrase "sea of electrons" describe?

   _____

   _____

4. An attraction between a positive metal ion and the electrons surrounding it is called a(n) _____.

Use the diagram below to answer questions 5–7 in the spaces provided.

5. What do points a and b represent?

   _____

6. What action is modeled by the diagram?

   _____

7. How does metallic bonding explain the result at point c?

   _____

   _____

   _____

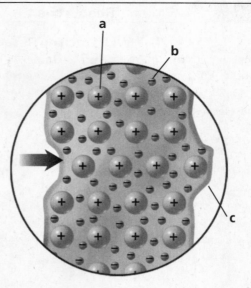

Atoms and Bonding · *Enrich*

How Hard Is Hard?

Some metals, such as copper and gold, are also minerals. A mineral is a naturally occurring solid that has a crystal structure and a definite chemical composition. Their crystal structure makes minerals hard. Nonetheless, there is considerable variation among minerals in hardness. Talc is the softest mineral, diamond is the hardest. Mohs Scale of Hardness, which is shown below, is used to classify minerals and other substances according to their hardnesses. An object on the scale will scratch anything with a lower number, but will be scratched by anything with a higher number. The table includes some everyday objects in parentheses for comparison.

Mineral (Object)	Hardness
talc	1
(asphalt)	1.3
gypsum	2
(fingernail)	2.5
calcite	3
(copper coin)	3
fluorite	4
apatite	5
(knife blade)	5.5
feldspar	6
(steel file)	6.5
quartz	7
topaz	8
corundum	9
diamond	10

Answer the following questions on a separate sheet of paper.

1. Which minerals will scratch quartz? How do you know?
2. According to the information in the table, do you think that you could scratch a copper coin with a knife blade? Explain your answer.
3. How could you determine the hardness rating for a mineral not listed on the scale?

Name _____ Date _____ Class _____

Atoms and Bonding • *Vocabulary Skill*

High-Use Academic Words

High-use words are words that are used frequently in academic reading, writing, and discussions.

Word	Definition	Example Sentence
conduct (kahn DUCT) p. 199	*v.* To allow something to travel along or through it	Metal strips on a circuit board <u>conduct</u> electric current.
stable (STAY bul) p. 177	*adj.* Not easily or quickly changed from one state to another	Gold is a <u>stable</u> metal that does not rust or tarnish.
structure (STRUK chur) p. 178	*n.* The way in which parts of something are put together	The outside <u>structure</u> of the building is made of brick and concrete.
symbol (SIM bul) p. 187	*n.* A written sign that stands for something else	The <u>symbol</u> for the element oxygen is O.

Apply It!

From the table above choose the word that best completes each sentence. Then answer question 4.

1. The patient was breathing regularly and in a _____ condition.
2. The chemistry teacher wrote the _____ for silver on the board.
3. The metal handle of the frying pan will _____ heat.
4. What meaning of stable might apply to a structure?

Key Terms

Answer the questions by writing the correct Key Terms in the blanks. Use the numbered letters in the terms to find the hidden Key Term. Then write a definition for the hidden Key Term.

Clues   **Key Terms**

What type of bonding is found in
gold or copper?

__ __ __ __ __ __ __ __
                                    1

What is a covalent bond called in
which electrons are shared unequally?

__ __ __ __ __
    2

_____ electrons
are involved in bonding.

__ __ __ __ __ __ __
    3

What is a mixture called that is made
of more than one element and has the
properties of a metal?

__ __ __ __ __
    4

A _____ is a neutral group of atoms
joined by covalent bonds.

__ __ __ __ __ __ __
        5   6

What is an atom or group of atoms
that has become electrically charged?

__ __ __
        7

What is an orderly, three-dimensional
arrangement formed by ions called?

__ __ __ __ __ __ __
                    8

What is the attraction between two
oppositely charged ions called?

__ __ __ __ __ __ __ __
                        9

A bond in which electrons are
shared equally is _____.

__ __ __ __ __ __ __
    10 11

What is a bond in which two pairs
of electrons are shared between atoms?

__ __ __ __ __ __ __ __ __
    12

Key Term: __ __ __ __ __ __ __ __ __ __ __ __
            1 2 3 4 5 6 7 8   9 10 11 12

Definition:

_____

_____

Atoms and Bonding · *Pre-Assessment*

Write the letter of the correct answer on the line at the left.

____ 1. The atom is made of protons, electrons, and
      a. valence electrons.   **b.** neutrons.
      c. molecules.   **d.** ions.

____ 2. Reactant atoms and molecules interact to form
      a. products with identical physical properties.
      b. products with different physical properties.
      c. products with identical chemical properties.
      d. products with different chemical properties.

____ 3. In chemical reactions, the number of atoms
      a. varies according to the elements involved.
      b. changes from one reactant to another.
      c. stays the same.
      d. depends on how the atoms are arranged.

____ 4. Compounds are formed by
      a. combining two or more different elements.
      b. bombarding atoms with high-speed particles.
      c. combining two or more different nuclei
      d. dissolving a solid in a liquid.

Atoms and Bonding · *Section 5.1 Quiz*

If the statement is true, write true. *If it is false, change the underlined word or words to make the statement true.*

_____ 1. The number of <u>protons</u> in an atom of an element determines the ways in which the atom can bond with other atoms.

_____ 2. Atoms of most elements are more stable when they have <u>eight</u> electrons.

_____ 3. Elements within a group have similar properties because they all have the same number of <u>ions</u> in their atoms.

_____ 4. All the inert gases except <u>krypton</u> have eight valence electrons.

_____ 5. Hydrogen is placed above Group 1 in the periodic table because it has only <u>two protons</u>.

Name _____ Date _____ Class _____

Atoms and Bonding · *Section 5.2 Quiz*

Fill in the blank to complete each statement.

1. Most atoms with one, two, or three valence electrons can _____ electrons and become more stable.
2. When an atom gains an electron, it gains a _____ charge and becomes a _____ ion.
3. You can tell the ratio of ions in an ionic compound by looking at the compound's _____.
4. Ionic compounds form solids by building up _____ of ions.
5. When ionic crystals dissolve in water, the bonds between ions are broken, so the solution _____ electric current.

Atoms and Bonding

Name _____ Date _____ Class _____

Atoms and Bonding · *Section 5.3 Quiz*

If the statement is true, write true. *If it is false, change the underlined word or words to make the statement true.*

_____ 1. Covalent bonds usually form between atoms of <u>a metal and nonmetal</u>.

_____ 2. The attraction of <u>each atom's nucleus for the shared pair of electrons</u> holds atoms together in a covalent bond.

_____ 3. Double and triple bonds can form when atoms share more than one pair of <u>properties</u>.

_____ 4. Compared to ionic compounds, molecular compounds generally have lower <u>temperature and pressure</u>.

_____ 5. The unequal sharing of electrons in a polar bond makes the atom with the stronger pull slightly <u>negative</u>.

© Pearson Education, Inc., publishing as Pearson Prentice Hall. All rights reserved.

Name _____ Date _____ Class _____

Atoms and Bonding · *Section 5.4 Quiz*

Fill in the blank to complete each statement.

1. Most metals you see in everyday life are made of _____.
2. Iron is often alloyed to make steel because iron objects _____ when they are exposed to air.
3. Most metals are _____ solids.
4. Many properties of solid metals can be explained by the _____ model of metallic bonding.
5. Five properties of metals that are related to the behavior of valence electrons are _____, _____, _____, _____, and _____.

Atoms, Bonding, and the Periodic Table
Review and Reinforce

1. 7
2. 7
3. 5
4. It is reactive because it needs three valence electrons to become stable.
5. Nonmetal
6. Valence electrons have the highest energy and are most loosely held by the atom
7. chemical bond
8. Electrons may be transferred or shared between atoms.
9. If atoms of an element have less than eight valence electrons, the element will likely react with other elements.
10. the same number of valence electrons
11. lose
12. gain; share

Atoms, Bonding, and the Periodic Table
Enrich

1. Groups 1 and 2; because they are very reactive
2. The noble gases; because they do not react easily
3. You need one fuse to ignite the gunpowder that sends the rocket into the air, and other fuses to ignite the chemical compounds that produce the light and noise once the rocket has reached its maximum height.
4. The element in solution might burn as it does in a firework rocket, giving off a color. The results could be used to tell the solutions apart.

Ionic Bonds
Review and Reinforce

1. An atom becomes a positive ion by losing an electron. An atom becomes a negative ion by gaining an electron.
2. Oppositely charged ions are attracted to each other. When ionic bonds form, the ions come together in a way that balances out the charges on the ions.
3. Solid ionic compounds typically form hard, brittle crystals and have high melting points. They conduct electricity well when dissolved in water or melted.

4. As solids, the ions are tightly bound in ionic bonds. The ions are free to move when the compound is dissolved in water. Then electricity can flow.
5. Two. A sulfide ion has a charge of 2–. Since potassium ions only have a charge of 1+, two potassium ions are needed to balance the charge.
6. $CaCl_2$, K_3PO_4
7. Magnesium sulfide, ammonium chloride, and potassium oxide
8. Ammonium and phosphate are polyatomic.
9. An atom or group of atoms that has an electrical charge
10. The attraction between oppositely charged ions
11. In a crystal, positive and negative ions alternate, forming an orderly three-dimensional arrangement.

Ionic Bonds
Enrich

1. Atomic radius increases from top to bottom; atomic radius decreases from left to right.
2. Cesium; barium; These two should be the most reactive of their groups because each has the largest atomic radius in its group. The element with the largest atomic radius holds some of its electrons less tightly, so the electrons are easier to remove.
3. The Group 1 element is more reactive in each case because the atomic radius of the Group 1 element is larger than the atomic radius of the corresponding Group 2 element. This means an atom of a Group 1 element holds onto some of its electrons less tightly, so less energy is required to remove the electrons. Also, two electrons must be removed from atoms of elements in Group 2, which would require more energy than needed to remove one electron from Group 1 atoms.
4. The decreasing atomic radii across a period (through Group 17) cause the atoms of elements in Groups 3 through 13 to hold their electrons more tightly than do the atoms of elements in Groups 1 and 2. To remove an electron and get these elements to react would require larger amounts of energy.

Covalent Bonds
Review and Reinforce

1. Students should have drawn one circle around the shared electrons in each diagram (two electron pairs shared in O_2 and three pairs in N_2).

2. The bond in O_2

3. The bond in N_2

4. N_2, O_2, and F_2 have nonpolar bonds.

5. The polar bond is a result of the fluorine atom pulling more strongly on the shared electrons than the hydrogen atom does.

6. Compared to ionic compounds, molecular compounds have lower melting and boiling points. Most molecular compounds are poor conductors of electricity when melted or dissolved.

7. nonpolar

8. polar

9. polar

10. nonpolar

Covalent Bonds
Enrich

1. Because oil is nonpolar, it will not mix with polar water. It will only float on the water's surface. This allows floating barriers to keep oil contained until it can be removed with nets. If oil mixed with water, it could not be separated from water as easily.

2. Because the bonds are between two of the same kind of atom, these atoms pull equally on the electrons involved in the bond. That means the bonds are nonpolar.

3. One end of each detergent molecule attracts water molecules, while the other end attracts oil molecules. This attraction pulls apart a large oil spill bit by bit.

4. No. No matter how small the oil particles are, they will never mix with the water, because oil is nonpolar and water is polar. Even if they look like they are mixed, the oil and water will eventually separate.

Bonding in Metals
Review and Reinforce

1. Ability to conduct heat and electricity, ability to change shape easily, and luster

2. An alloy is a mixture made of two or mor elements that has the properties of metal.

3. The phrase describes the valence electron of metal atoms that drift freely around the atoms in a sample of a metal.

4. metallic bond

5. Point (a) represents positively charged metal ions. Point (b) represents freely moving valence electrons.

6. Striking or hammering a metal to make it change shape

7. In metallic bonding, metal ions are attracted to the freely moving electrons all around them and not to other metal ions. The ions can be pushed away from one another, bu the metallic bonds hold the ions close enough together that the metal does not break.

Bonding in Metals
Enrich

1. Topaz, corundum, and diamond; they have a higher rating on the Mohs scale.

2. Yes, according to the table you could scratch a copper coin with a knife blade because the knife blade has a higher rating on the Mohs scale.

3. You would find the mineral on the scale with the highest hardness rating that the unlisted one will scratch. Then find the mineral on the scale with the lowest hardness that will scratch the unlisted one. The hardness of the unlisted mineral would be a number between those two hardness ratings.

Key Terms

Key Terms: metallic, polar, valence, alloy, molecule, ion, crystal, ionic bond, nonpolar, double bond
Hidden Key Term: covalent bond
Definition: A chemical bond formed when two atoms share electrons

Vocabulary Skill

1. stable
2. symbol
3. conduct
4. not easily moved, firm

Pre-Assessment

1. B
2. D
3. C
4. A

Section 5.1 Quiz

1. valence electrons
2. true
3. valence electrons
4. helium
5. only one valence electron

Section 5.2 Quiz

1. lose
2. negative; negative
3. chemical formula
4. repeating patterns
5. conducts

Section 5.3 Quiz

1. nonmetals
2. rue
3. electrons
4. boiling points and melting points
5. rue

Section 5.4 Quiz

1. alloys
2. rust
3. crystalline
4. "sea of electrons"
5. malleability; ductility; luster; electrical conductivity; thermal conductivity

Chapter 6 Chemical Reactions

Observing Chemical Change

🕐 *4 periods, 2 blocks*

Objectives

6.1.1 State how changes in matter can be described.

6.1.2 Explain how you can tell when a chemical reaction occurs.

🌐 California Standards

❏ S 8.5.a
❏ S 8.5.c

PRETEACH

Build Background Knowledge
Students name familiar changes in matter as an introduction to the physical and chemical changes they will read about in the section.

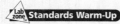 Standards Warm-Up *What Happens When Chemicals React?* **L1**

Resources

❏ **Vocabulary Flashcards**
  L2 Chapter 6 Vocabulary
❏ **Build Science Vocabulary** *Online*
  L2 Chapter 6 Vocabulary

INSTRUCT

Matter and Change Introduce physical and chemical properties of matter by discussing several examples.

Evidence for Chemical Reactions Describe the two main types of observable chemical change, and have students identify them in the reaction between magnesium and oxygen.

 Skills Lab   *Where's the Evidence?* **L2**

Resources

❏ **Reading/Notetaking Guides**
  (Adapted versions available)
  Chapter 6, Section 1
❏ **Color Transparencies Book**
  L2 PS58, PS59
❏ **Laboratory Manual**
  L2 *Where's the Evidence?*
  Student Worksheets
❏ **Lab Activity DVD Library**
  L2 Skills Lab: *Where's the Evidence?*
❏ **Student Edition in MP3 Format**
❏ **Spanish Section Summaries in MP3 Format**
❏ **www.SciLinks.org** Web Code: scn-1221

ASSESS/REMEDIATE

Assess Progress
Evaluate student comprehension with the Section Assessment and Section Quiz.

Remediation
Students create a graphic organizer showing causes and evidence for chemical changes.

Resources

❏ **Teaching Resources, Unit 2**
  L2 Section 6.1 Quiz
  L1 6.1 Review and Reinforce, ELL, LPR, SN
  L3 6.1 Enrich, AR, GT

Chemical Reactions · *Review and Reinforce*

Observing Chemical Change

Understanding Main Ideas

Complete the following table. Describe changes in properties that you might notice during each process and state whether the changes are chemical or physical.

Changes in Matter		
Event	**Observable Changes**	**Type of Change**
Baking a cake	1.	2.
Burning a log	3.	4.
Freezing water	5.	6.

Building Vocabulary

From the list below, choose the term that best completes each sentence.

matter   physical change
chemical change   endothermic reaction
chemistry   exothermic reaction
precipitate

7. Any change that alters a substance without changing it into another substance is a(n) _____.

8. _____ is anything that has mass and takes up space.

9. A reaction that releases energy in the form of heat is called a(n) _____.

10. A(n) _____ is a reaction in which energy is absorbed.

11. A chemical change is also referred to as a(n) _____.

12. A(n) _____ is a solid formed from a solution during a chemical reaction.

13. _____ is the study of the properties of matter and how matter changes.

Chemical Reactions • *Enrich*

Separation Science

A mixture is a combination of two or more pure substances, and the substances do not combine to form new material. Therefore, you should be able to separate a mixture into the substances that make it. There are several ways to separate mixtures. Figure 1 shows a mixture of sand and water being separated by *filtration*. The salt in a solution of salt water can be separated by *evaporation*, shown in Figure 2. When you let the sand particles in a mixture of sand and water settle to the bottom of a container, then carefully pour the water off into another container, you are using a method called *decanting*, shown in Figure 3.

Study the following illustrations, then answer the questions below on a separate sheet of paper.

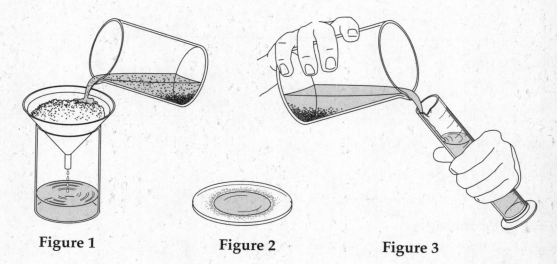

Figure 1   Figure 2   Figure 3

1. Using Figure 1, explain the process of filtration. Give another example of filtration used to separate a mixture.

2. Discuss a use for evaporation.

3. What types of mixtures could be separated by decanting? Is laboratory equipment necessary for decanting a mixture? Why or why not?

4. Would a separation of the types described above cause a chemical change or a physical change? Explain your answer.

Describing Chemical Reactions

⏰ *2 periods, 1 block*

Objectives

2.1   Identify what information a chemical equation contains.
2.2   Explain how matter is conserved during a chemical reaction.
2.3   Explain what a balanced chemical equation must show.
2.4   Name three types of chemical reactions.

🌐 California Standards
❑ S 8.5.b

PRETEACH

Build Background Knowledge
Students brainstorm familiar symbols and explain how symbols are helpful, as an introduction to the use of symbols to describe chemical reactions.

🔺 **Standards Warm-Up** *Do You Lose Anything?* **L2**

Resources
❑ **Vocabulary Flashcards**
    L2 Chapter 6 Vocabulary
❑ **Build Science Vocabulary** *Online*
    L2 Chapter 6 Vocabulary

INSTRUCT

What Are Chemical Equations? Show students the general plan of all chemical equations.
Conservation of Matter Ask questions about the figure showing the reaction of iron and sulfur to guide students in understanding the principle of conservation of matter.
Balancing Chemical Equations Explain why chemical equations must be balanced, and show students how to balance a sample equation.
Classifying Chemical Reactions Have students read about categories of chemical reactions and then apply the concepts by classifying several sample chemical reactions.

Resources
❑ **Reading/Notetaking Guides**
    (Adapted versions available)
    Chapter 6, Section 2
❑ **Color Transparencies Book**
    L2 PS60, PS98, PS61, PS62
❑ **Student Edition in MP3 Format**
❑ **Spanish Section Summaries in MP3 Format**
❑ **www.SciLinks.org** Web Code: cgp-2022

ASSESS/REMEDIATE

Assess Progress
Evaluate student comprehension with the Section Assessment and Section Quiz.

Remediation
Students help make a table comparing and contrasting synthesis, degradation, and replacement reactions.

Resources
❑ **Teaching Resources, Unit 2**
    L2 Section 6.2 Quiz
    L1 6.2 Review and Reinforce, ELL, LPR, SN
    L3 6.2 Enrich, AR, GT

Name _____ Date _____ Class _____

Chemical Reactions · Review and Reinforce

Describing Chemical Reactions

Understanding Main Ideas

Balance the equations on the lines below. State whether the reaction is a synthesis, decomposition, or replacement reaction.

Given Equation	Balanced Equation	Type of Reaction
1. $FeS + HCl \rightarrow FeCl_2 + H_2S$	a.	b.
2. $Na + F_2 \rightarrow NaF$	a.	b.
3. $HgO \rightarrow Hg + O_2$	a.	b.

Answer questions 4 and 5 on a separate sheet of paper.

4. Describe in words the reaction represented by the equation: $2 H_2 + O_2 \rightarrow 2 H_2O$. Include a description of the composition of each kind of molecule.
5. Use the principle of conservation of mass to explain why the equation in question 4 is balanced.

Building Vocabulary

Match each term with its definition by writing the letter of the correct definition on the line beside the term in the left column.

____ 6. chemical equation

____ 7. decomposition

____ 8. coefficient

____ 9. product

____ 10. reactant

____ 11. conservation of matter

____ 12. synthesis

____ 13. replacement

a. substance present after a reaction

b. reaction in which substances combine to form a more complex compound

c. uses symbols and formulas to show chemical reactions

d. reaction in which one element replaces another in a compound

e. substance present before a reaction

f. number telling how many molecules of a substance are involved in a chemical reaction

g. reaction in which compounds are broken down into simpler products

h. principle that states that matter is not created or destroyed during a chemical reaction

The Decomposition of Water

You learned in Section 2 that hydrogen gas and oxygen gas can react to produce water. The reverse of this reaction can also occur. In other words, water can be broken down to make hydrogen gas and oxygen gas. The breakdown of water is a decomposition reaction. The unbalanced equation for this reaction is shown below.

$$H_2O \rightarrow H_2 + O_2$$
Water   Hydrogen gas   Oxygen gas

For this reaction to occur, there must be an electric current through the water as shown in the figure below. Two wires are connected to a battery, and the free ends of the wires are put into a beaker of water that contains a small amount of sulfuric acid. The sulfuric acid helps to increase the flow of current through the water.

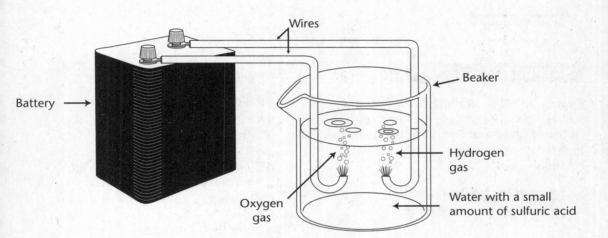

Answer the following questions on a separate sheet of paper.

1. Write a balanced equation for the decomposition of water.

2. How many atoms of hydrogen are on the left side of the balanced equation? How many oxygen atoms? How many hydrogen atoms are on the right side of the balanced equation? How many oxygen atoms?

3. The water in a beaker has a mass of 200 g. An electric current is turned on in the water for two hours. Afterward the water has a mass of only 176 g. What happened to the missing mass?

4. Suppose a sample of water decomposes to make 4 g of hydrogen gas and 32 g of oxygen gas. What mass of water decomposed? How do you know?

5. Look at the figure above. How can you tell that a reaction is occurring?

Controlling Chemical Reactions

🕐 *2 periods, 1 block*

ABILITY LEVELS KEY
L1 Basic to Average
L2 For All Students
L3 Average to Advance

Objectives
6.3.1   Explain how activation energy is related to chemical reactions.
6.3.2   Identify factors that affect the rate of a chemical reaction.

🌐 California Standards
❑ S 8.5.a
❑ S 8.5.c

PRETEACH

Build Background Knowledge
Students infer from a familiar example how temperature affects the rate of chemical reactions.

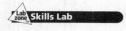 *Can You Speed Up or Slow Down a Reaction?* **L2**

Resources
❑ **Vocabulary Flashcards**
   L2 Chapter 6 Vocabulary
❑ **Build Science Vocabulary** *Online*
   L2 Chapter 6 Vocabulary

INSTRUCT

Energy and Reactions Use a questioning strategy to define and explain activation energy.
Rates of Chemical Reactions List and discuss four factors that affect rates of chemical reactions.

Skills Lab   *Temperature and Enzyme Activity* **L3**

Resources
❑ **Reading/Notetaking Guides**
   (Adapted versions available)
   Chapter 6, Section 3
❑ **Color Transparencies Book**
   L2 PS64, PS66
❑ **Laboratory Manual**
   L2 *Temperature and Enzyme Activity*
   Student Worksheets
❑ **Lab Activity DVD Library**
   L2 Skills Lab: *Temperature and Enzyme Activity*
❑ **Student Edition in MP3 Format**
❑ **Spanish Section Summaries in MP3 Format**

ASSESS/REMEDIATE

Assess Progress
Evaluate student comprehension with the Section Assessment and Section Quiz.
Remediation
Students define the key terms.

Resources
❑ **Teaching Resources, Unit 2**
   L2 Section 6.3 Quiz
   L1 6.3 Review and Reinforce, ELL, LPR, SN
   L3 6.3 Enrich, AR, GT

Name _____ Date _____ Class _____

Controlling Chemical Reactions

Understanding Main Ideas

Use the figures below to answer questions 1–3. Write your answers on a separate sheet of paper.

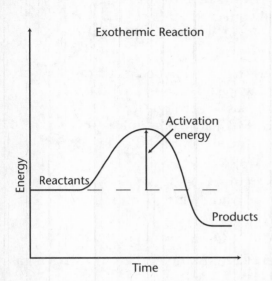

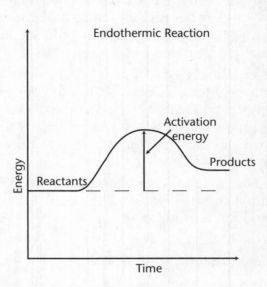

1. Use what you know about endothermic and exothermic reactions to explain the differences in the graphs above.

2. Why is the activation energy pictured as a hill in the two diagrams?

3. Explain how adding heat to the reactions shown in the diagram would change the rate of these chemical reactions. Name two other ways to change the rate of a chemical reaction.

Building Vocabulary

Write a definition for each of the following terms on the lines below.

4. concentration _____

_____

5. enzyme _____

_____

6. inhibitor _____

_____

Name _____ Date _____ Class _____

Flameless Ration Heaters

Suppose that you are a soldier on patrol far from your base camp. The weather is very cold and you wish you had something warm to eat. However, you aren't carrying a camp stove and it would be too dangerous to light a fire because its smoke would reveal your position. Luckily, you have a *Meal Ready to Eat* (MRE) and a *Flameless Ration Heater* (FRH) in your backpack. (A ration is a portion of food.)

An MRE is a meal, such as beef stew, inside a special pouch made of aluminum foil and plastic. To heat your MRE, you slide it into an FRH, as shown in the figure below. An FRH is a kind of plastic envelope that contains certain chemicals. When you add water to the FRH, an exothermic reaction occurs. The heat produced by this reaction warms up your meal in about 15 minutes.

The chemicals inside an FRH include magnesium (Mg), iron (Fe), and sodium chloride (NaCl). The reaction that takes place when water is added to an FRH is as follows.

$$Mg \quad + \quad 2H_2O \quad \rightarrow \quad Mg(OH)_2 \quad + \quad H_2$$

Magnesium   Water   Magnesium hydroxide   Hydrogen gas

The reaction of magnesium and water is normally very slow. As a result, it gives off heat very slowly. In an FRH, however, this reaction occurs much faster and so it gives off heat much faster as well.

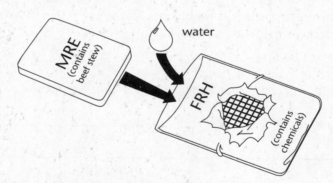

Answer the following questions on a separate sheet of paper.

1. Iron and sodium chloride are present in an FRH, but they are not reactants in the equation shown above. Why do you think they are included in an FRH?

2. Why do you think an FRH doesn't come with water already in it?

3. Do you think there are small pieces or large pieces of magnesium metal in an FRH? Explain.

4. Why is it important that the reaction in an FRH be fast?

Fire and Fire Safety

🕐 *1 period, 1/2 block*

Objectives

6.4.1   List the three things necessary to maintain a fire.

6.4.2   Explain why you should know about the causes of fire and how to prevent a fire.

🌐 California Standards

❑ S 8.5.c

PRETEACH

Build Background Knowledge
Students share experiences they have had with fire and recall fire safety rules they have learned.

 **Standards Warm-Up** *How Does Baking Soda Affect a Fire?* **L2**

Resources

❑ **Vocabulary Flashcards**
   L2 Chapter 6 Vocabulary
❑ **Build Science Vocabulary** *Online*
   L2 Chapter 6 Vocabulary

INSTRUCT

Understanding Fire Use the fire triangle to show students what every fire needs to burn.
Home Fire Safety Review methods for fighting fires and how to prevent injuries and deaths from fires.

Resources

❑ **Reading/Notetaking Guides**
   (Adapted versions available)
   Chapter 6, Section 4
❑ **Color Transparencies Book**
   L2 PS68, PS69
❑ **Student Edition in MP3 Format**
❑ **Spanish Section Summaries in MP3 Format**
❑ **www.SciLinks.org** Web Code: scn-1224

ASSESS/REMEDIATE

Assess Progress
Evaluate student comprehension with the Section Assessment and Section Quiz.

Remediation
Students name fire-prevention and fire safety features of a fire-safe house.

Resources

❑ **Teaching Resources, Unit 2**
   L2 Section 6.4 Quiz
   L1 6.4 Review and Reinforce, ELL, LPR, SN
   L3 6.4 Enrich, AR, GT

Chemical Reactions

Chemical Reactions • *Review and Reinforce*

Fire and Fire Safety

Understanding Main Ideas

Use the illustration to answer questions 1 and 2 in the spaces provided.

1. What are the three points of the fire triangle shown in the illustration?

   _____

   _____

   _____

   _____

2. Name one way you can stop this small stove fire safely. Also explain how this method would remove a part of the fire triangle.

   _____

   _____

   _____

   _____

   _____

Write your answers to questions 3 and 4 in the spaces provided.

3. Name two fire safety tips you should practice in your kitchen.

   _____

   _____

   _____

4. What should you do when a fire continues to grow while you are fighting it?

   _____

   _____

Building Vocabulary

Answer the following questions in the spaces provided.

5. What is combustion?

   _____

   _____

6. What is a fuel? What are some examples of fuels?

   _____

   _____

Chemical Reactions · *Enrich*

Fighting Forest Fires

Each year thousands of forest fires occur throughout the United States. There are many methods used to control forest fires, but all rely on breaking the fire triangle of heat, fuel, and oxygen.

Some methods of fire control begin long before a forest fire starts. For example, firebreaks can be used to divide a forest into smaller sections. A *firebreak* is a strip of land that has been cleared of trees and other plants. Firebreaks are wide enough that a fire in one section of the forest usually cannot "jump" across them to other sections.

Another method of prevention used before a forest fire starts involves setting fires on purpose. Firefighters set small fires in areas of a forest where large amounts of fuel such as fallen branches and leaves have built up on the forest floor. These fires are called *controlled burns.* Firefighters closely watch controlled burns so that they can put the fires out before they grow too large. By reducing the amount of fuel available, controlled burns actually help to protect the forest.

In addition, firefighters sometimes set small fires during a forest fire to help bring a large forest fire under control. These fires, called *backfires,* are set in between a firebreak and an approaching forest fire. Backfires help to control a forest fire by reducing the amount of fuel in its path.

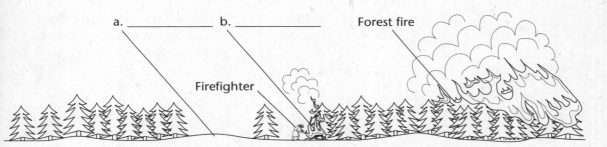

Answer the following questions on a separate sheet of paper.

1. Label the type of fire control pictured in the diagram above by filling in the blanks.

2. What keeps a forest fire from "jumping" across a firebreak?

3. Firefighters sometimes add chemicals called wetting agents to the water that they spray on forest fires. *Wetting agents* increase the ability of water to penetrate or seep into wood. Why do you think this helps to control a fire?

4. In remote areas, firefighters may have only a limited water supply available to spray on fires. In these cases, firefighters may shovel dirt onto the flames. How do you think dirt helps to put out a fire?

Chemical Reactions • *Vocabulary Skill*

Identify Multiple Meanings

Some familiar words have more than one meaning. Words you use everyday may have different meanings in science.

Word	Everyday Meaning	Scientific Meaning
concentration	*n.* Close attention for a long period of time. **Example:** Studying with the TV on affects her <u>concentration</u>.	*n.* The amount of a substance in a given volume **Example:** Most soft drinks contain a high <u>concentration</u> of sugar.
matter	*n.* The subject of discussion, concern or action **Example:** The subject <u>matter</u> of the movie was space exploration.	*n.* Anything that has mass and takes up space. **Example:** Three states of <u>matter</u> are solids, liquids, and gases.
product	*n.* Anything that is made or created **Example:** Milk and cheese are dairy <u>products</u>.	*n.* A substance formed as a result of a chemical reaction **Example:** In a chemical reaction, substances can combine to form one or more <u>products</u>.

Apply It!

Complete the sentences below with the correct word from the table above, and tell whether the everyday or scientific meaning is used. Then answer question 5.

1. When the ice cube melted it changed the form of its _____ from solid to liquid.
2. The student committee discussed the _____ of the upcoming prom.
3. This new _____ is an excellent floor cleaner.
4. The two different substances combined to form a brand new _____.
5. Use a dictionary to find another everyday meaning for **matter** and use it in a sentence.

Name _____ Date _____ Class _____

Key Terms

Complete the sentences by using one of the scrambled terms below.

mocpsoinoited	dcsutrop	emtrsyhci	msubocniot	ysisehtns
neefiticcof	ntreactonionc	etaptiicrpe	tyltsaac	ctatsnaer
nioatvicat	rtiohbiin	eaeeplcmnrt		

1. A material that increases the rate of a reaction by lowering the activation energy is called a(n) _____.

2. A chemical reaction that breaks down compounds into simpler products is called a(n) _____ reaction.

3. A solid that forms from solution during a chemical reaction is called a(n) _____.

4. The materials you have at the beginning of a chemical reaction are called _____.

5. A chemical reaction in which two or more substances combine to make a more complex compound is called a(n) _____ reaction.

6. The amount of one material in a given volume of another material is called _____.

7. A material used to decrease the rate of a reaction is called a(n) _____.

8. A rapid reaction between oxygen and a fuel is called _____.

9. The minimum amount of energy needed to start a chemical reaction is called the _____ energy.

10. A chemical reaction in which one element replaces another in a compound, or in which two elements in different compounds trade places, is called a(n) _____ reaction.

11. The substances formed as a result of a chemical reaction are called _____.

12. A number placed in front of a chemical formula in a chemical equation is called a(n) _____.

13. The study of the properties of matter and how matter changes is called _____.

Chemical Reactions ▪ *Math Skills*

Math Skills

Balance the chemical equations below by adding coefficients. Write the balanced equations on the lines provided.

Balancing Chemical Equations

1. $H_2O \rightarrow H_2 + O_2$

   _____

2. $N_2 + H_2 \rightarrow NH_3$

   _____

3. $C_3H_8 + O_2 \rightarrow CO_2 + H_2O$

   _____

4. $K + H_2O \rightarrow H_2 + KOH$

   _____

5. $Li + O_2 \rightarrow Li_2O$

   _____

6. $Fe + O_2 \rightarrow Fe_2O_3$

   _____

7. $Ag + N_2 \rightarrow Ag_3N$

   _____

8. $C_2H_5OH + O_2 \rightarrow CO_2 + H_2O$

   _____

Chemical Reactions · *Pre-Assessment*

Write the letter of the correct answer on the line at the left.

_____ 1. Which of the following is an example of a physical change?

    a. Wood burns and becomes ash.

    b. A silver fork tarnishes.

    c. Water boils and becomes water vapor.

    d. Leaves decay over time.

_____ 2. When a forest burns, it

    a. neither absorbs nor releases energy.

    b. loses matter and energy.

    c. absorbs energy.

    d. releases energy.

_____ 3. Fe, which stands for iron, is a

    a. chemical symbol.   **b.** chemical equation.

    c. atomic number.   **d.** name

_____ 4. The ease and speed with which an element combines with other elements is called its

    a. atomic number.   **b.** chemical property.

    c. physical property.   **d.** reactivity.

Chemical Reactions · *Section 6.1 Quiz*

If the statement is true, write true. *If it is false, change the underlined word or words to make the statement true.*

_____ 1. Chemical reactions usually <u>absorb or liberate</u> heat.

_____ 2. To observe the chemical properties of a substance you must <u>observe it exactly as it is</u>.

_____ 3. When you tear a piece of bread, you cause a <u>physical change</u>.

_____ 4. Bonds between atoms break when a <u>physical change</u> takes place.

_____ 5. A precipitate is evidence for a <u>chemical reaction</u>.

Name _____ Date _____ Class _____

Chemical Reactions · *Section 6.2 Quiz*

Fill in the blank to complete each statement.

1. In a chemical equation, the _____ and _____ are written as chemical formulas.

2. The total mass of the reactants in a chemical reaction must equal the total mass of the products, in keeping with the _____.

3. A burning match is an example of a(n) _____, in which matter can enter from or escape to the surroundings.

4. A(n) _____ tells how many atoms or molecules of a reactant or a product take place in a chemical reaction.

5. Hydrogen peroxide (H_2O_2) decomposing into water and oxygen gas is a chemical reaction classified as _____.

Name _____ Date _____ Class _____

Chemical Reactions · *Section 6.3 Quiz*

If the statement is true, write true. *If it is false, change the underlined word or words to make the statement true.*

_____ 1. <u>Kinetic energy</u> is required to start a chemical reaction.

_____ 2. The <u>exothermic</u> reaction between baking soda and vinegar requires a continuous source of heat.

_____ 3. You can speed up a chemical reaction by increasing the number of molecules of the <u>reactants</u>.

_____ 4. You can slow down a chemical reaction by <u>decreasing</u> the temperature.

_____ 5. Your body's cells have biological <u>inhibitors</u> that lower the activation energy required for chemical reactions to take place.

Name _____ Date _____ Class _____

Chemical Reactions · *Section 6.4 Quiz*

Fill in the blank to complete each statement.

1. _____ of gasoline produces carbon dioxide and water.

2. Three things necessary to start and maintain a fire are _____, _____, and _____.

3. Water is effective in fighting fires because water removes two parts of the fire triangle: _____ and _____.

4. The three most common sources of home fires are _____, _____, and _____.

5. _____, which is released when baking soda is heated, can prevent contact between the fuel in a small fire and oxygen in the air.

Observing Chemical Change
Review and Reinforce

1. Answers may vary. Sample answer: Change in texture, from gooey liquid to dry and crumbly solid
2. Chemical change
3. Sample answer: Change in color, from brown log to black ashes
4. Chemical change
5. Sample answer: Change in state, from liquid water to solid ice
6. Physical change
7. physical change
8. Matter
9. exothermic reaction
10. endothermic reaction
11. chemical reaction
12. precipitate
13. Chemistry

Observing Chemical Change
Enrich

1. In filtration, a liquid-solid mixture is passed through a filter to remove solid particles from the mixture. Filters that you can install on your kitchen faucet or the type you buy and place inside a pitcher of drinking water use filtration to remove small particles.
2. Evaporation can be used to separate salt from sea water to produce fresh water and also salt for commercial purposes. This can be done by pumping the sea water into large, shallow holding tanks. When the water evaporates, the salt remains.
3. Mixtures that have solid particles large enough and heavy enough to settle out of the mixture on standing can be decanted. Decanting can be done almost anywhere because it does not require special equipment—only a container with a spout and another container to hold the separated liquid.
4. Separations of the types mentioned here cause physical changes because no new substances form. The individual substances you get after separation were present in the mixture at the start.

Describing Chemical Reactions
Review and Reinforce

1. a. $FeS + 2 HCl \rightarrow FeCl_2 + H_2S$
b. Replacement
2. a. $2 Na + F_2 \rightarrow 2 NaF$
b. Synthesis
3. a. $2 HgO \rightarrow 2 Hg + O_2$
b. Decomposition
4. Two molecules of hydrogen combine with one molecule of oxygen to form two molecules of water. Each hydrogen molecule consists of two hydrogen atoms, the oxygen molecule consists of two atoms of oxygen, and each water molecule is made of two hydrogen atoms bonded with one oxygen atom.
5. The conservation of mass states that mass is neither created nor destroyed during a chemical reaction. The equation is balanced because both the reactants and the product contain the same number of atoms of each element: 4 hydrogen atoms and 2 oxygen atoms.
6. c
7. g
8. f
9. a
10. e
11. h
12. b
13. d

Describing Chemical Reactions
Enrich

1. $2H_2O \rightarrow 2H_2 + O_2$
2. There are 4 hydrogen atoms and 2 oxygen atoms on each side of the equation.
3. The missing mass is due to oxygen gas and hydrogen gas that have escaped from the beaker. These gases are produced by the decomposition of water.
4. 36 g; the total mass of the reactants must equal the total mass of the products.
5. Gas bubbles are being produced.

Controlling Chemical Reactions
Review and Reinforce

1. In the graph of the exothermic reaction, the products are at a lower level of energy than the reactants. This is because an exothermic reaction releases energy. The products in the endothermic reaction are at a higher level of energy than the reactants. This is because an endothermic reaction absorbs energy.
2. Activation energy is the amount of energy that has to be added to start a reaction. With enough energy, reactants can get "over the hump" and form products.
3. Increasing the temperature of a reaction makes the reacting particles move faster, increasing the rate of the reaction. Other ways to increase the rate of a chemical reaction are increase the concentration of a reactant, increase the surface area of a solid reactant, or add a catalyst.
4. The amount of substance in a given volume
5. A biological catalyst
6. A material used to decrease the rate of a reaction

Controlling Chemical Reactions
Enrich

1. They are catalysts for the reaction.
2. If an FRH came with water already in it, the exothermic reaction would already have taken place and no more heat would be given off.
3. The smaller the pieces of magnesium, the larger their surface area. As the surface area of a reactant increases, so does the rate of reaction. For this reason, the pieces of magnesium in an FRH are probably very small.
4. It is important that the reaction be fast so that a large amount of heat will be given off in a short period of time. In this way, the MRE can be quickly heated to a fairly warm temperature.

Fire and Fire Safety
Review and Reinforce

1. Fuel (the food in the skillet), oxygen (in the air), and heat (from the stove)
2. Answers should include one of the following. You can stop a small stove fire safely with baking soda. This smothers the fire and combines with the liquid in the food to produce carbon dioxide. The carbon dioxide prevents contact between the fuel and oxygen. You can also stop a small stove fire safely by putting the lid on the skillet. This keeps the fuel from coming into contact with oxygen. You can stop a small stove fire by using a fire extinguisher. This also keeps the fuel from coming into contact with oxygen.
3. Answers may vary. Sample answers: Keep flammable things, like pot-holders, towels, and curtains, away from stove burners. Keep a box of baking soda in the kitchen to fight grease fires. Have at least one fire extinguisher in good working order and within easy reach in your home.
4. You should get away from the fire and call the fire department.
5. Combustion is a rapid reaction between oxygen and fuel. Fire is caused by combustion.
6. A fuel is a material that releases energy when it burns. Examples of fuels are oil, coal, wood, gasoline, and paper.

Fire and Fire Safety
Enrich

1. a. Firebreak
   b. Backfire
2. Because there are no trees or large plants in a firebreak, there is virtually no fuel available and the fire cannot cross it.
3. Wetting agents increase the ability of water to keep the wood from coming into contact with oxygen. Without oxygen, the wood cannot burn. Water also reduces the temperature of the fire.
4. Throwing dirt on the flames covers up the fire's fuel, preventing oxygen from coming into contact with it.

Vocabulary Skill

1. matter (scientific)
2. matter (everyday)
3. product (everyday)
4. product (scientific)
5. Sample answer: material to be read. There was no current reading matter in the dentist's office.

Key Terms

1. catalyst
2. decomposition
3. precipitate
4. reactants
5. synthesis
6. concentration
7. inhibitor
8. combustion
9. activation
10. replacement
11. products
12. coefficient
13. chemistry

Math Skills

1. $2 H_2O \rightarrow 2 H_2 + O_2$
2. $N_2 + 3 H_2 \rightarrow 2 NH_3$
3. $C_3H_8 + 5 O_2 \rightarrow 3 CO_2 + 4 H_2O$
4. $2 K + 2 H_2O \rightarrow H_2 + 2 KOH$
5. $4 Li + O_2 \rightarrow 2 Li_2O$
6. $4 Fe + 3 O_2 \rightarrow 2 Fe_2O_3$
7. $6 Ag + N_2 \rightarrow 2 Ag_3N$
8. $C_2H_5OH + 3 O_2 \rightarrow 2 CO_2 + 3 H_2O$

Pre-Assessment

1. C
2. D
3. A
4. D

Section 6.1 Quiz

1. true
2. change it to another substance
3. true
4. chemical change
5. true

Section 6.2 Quiz

1. reactants; products
2. conservation of matter
3. open system
4. coefficient
5. decomposition

Section 6.3 Quiz

1. Activation energy
2. endothermic
3. true
4. true
5. catalysts

Section 6.4 Quiz

1. Combustion
2. fuel; oxygen; heat
3. fuel; heat
4. small heaters; cooking; faulty electrical wiring
5. Carbon dioxide gas

Chapter 7 Acids, Bases, and Solutions

Understanding Solutions

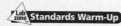 *2 periods, 1 block*

Objectives

7.1.1 State the characteristics of solutions, colloids, and suspensions.

7.1.2 Describe what happens to the particles of a solute when a solution forms.

7.1.3 Explain how solutes affect the freezing point and boiling point of a solvent.

California Standards
❑ S 8.5.d

PRETEACH

Build Background Knowledge
Students describe mixing sugar and water.

Lab zone Standards Warm-Up *What Makes a Mixture a Solution?* **L2**

Resources
❑ **Vocabulary Flashcards**
  L2 Chapter 7 Vocabulary
❑ **Build Science Vocabulary** *Online*
  L2 Chapter 7 Vocabulary

INSTRUCT

What Is a Solution? Explain what a solution is and which substance in a solution is the solute and which is the solvent.

Colloids and Suspensions Define colloids and suspensions, and challenge students to explain how they could separate a solute from a suspension.

Particles in a Solution Compare and contrast solutions of ionic compounds and molecular compounds.

Effects of Solutes on Solvents Use differences in taste to introduce the concept that solutes affect the properties of solvents.

Resources
❑ **Reading/Notetaking Guides**
  (Adapted versions available)
  Chapter 7, Section 1
❑ **Color Transparencies Book**
  L2 PS72
❑ **Student Edition in MP3 Format**
❑ **Spanish Section Summaries in MP3 Format**
❑ **www.SciLinks.org** Web Code: cgp-2031

ASSESS/REMEDIATE

Assess Progress
Evaluate student comprehension with the Section Assessment and Section Quiz.

Remediation
Students fill in details in an outline of the section.

Resources
❑ **Teaching Resources, Unit 2**
  L2 Section 7.1 Quiz
  L1 7.1 Review and Reinforce, ELL, LPR, SN
  L3 7.1 Enrich, AR, GT

Name _____ Date _____ Class _____

Acids, Bases, and Solutions • *Review and Reinforce*

Understanding Solutions

Understanding Main Ideas

Study the three mixtures below. Identify each mixture as a solution, colloid, or suspension. Explain.

Water and fine sand →

Mixture 1

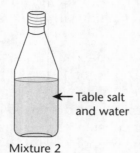
← Table salt and water

Mixture 2

← Milk

Mixture 3

1. _____

2. _____

3. _____

Answer the following questions on a separate sheet of paper.

4. Compare and contrast what happens to the particles of a ionic solid and a molecular solid when each mixes with water.

5. What are two ways that solutes affect the properties of solvents?

Building Vocabulary

From the list below, choose the term that best completes each sentence.

suspension   colloid

solute   solvent

solution

6. The part of a solution that is present in the smaller amount is the
   _____.

7. The part of a solution that is present in the larger amount is the
   _____.

8. A(n) _____ is a mixture containing small, undissolved particles that do not settle out, but are large enough to scatter light.

9. A mixture in which particles can be seen and easily separated by settling or filtration is called a(n) _____.

10. A well-mixed mixture that contains a solvent and at least one solute is called a(n) _____.

Name_____ Date_____ Class_____

The Chemistry of Ice Cream

A colloid is similar to a suspension in that its particles are larger than those of a solution. However, the particles of a colloid, like those of a solution, are small enough that they cannot be separated by settling or filtration. The particles in a colloid are said to be *dispersed*, rather than dissolved or suspended. Familiar colloids include shaving cream, whipped cream, fog, and smoke.

Ice cream is another familiar colloid. The particles in this colloid are solid fat, tiny crystals of ice, and droplets of water. A high concentration of sugars, salts, and proteins is dissolved in the water. Here, air acts something like a solvent. The particles of ice cream are dispersed in many tiny bubbles of air. Ice cream also contains other substances that allow "unlike" compounds to mix and stay mixed under the proper conditions. The unlike compounds in ice cream are water, which is polar, and fat, which is nonpolar.

The colloid formed by ice cream remains stable only at cold temperatures. When ice cream is warmed above freezing, its dispersed particles absorb energy and begin to move faster. When the fast-moving particles collide, they sometimes stick together. Eventually, the particles grow so large that they can no longer remain dispersed, and they settle out of the colloid.

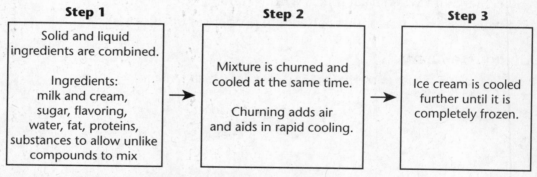

Step 1
Solid and liquid ingredients are combined.

Ingredients:
milk and cream, sugar, flavoring, water, fat, proteins, substances to allow unlike compounds to mix

Step 2
Mixture is churned and cooled at the same time.

Churning adds air and aids in rapid cooling.

Step 3
Ice cream is cooled further until it is completely frozen.

Answer the following questions on a separate sheet of paper.

1. Suppose the liquid water in ice cream did not have solutes dissolved in it. What effect do you think this would have on ice cream? (*Hint:* Consider the temperature at which ice cream is kept.)

2. What do you think happens to the air in the colloid when ice cream melts?

3. Look at the diagram above. Why do you think air isn't added until Step 2 when the mixture is cooled?

4. Milk is also a colloid. It consists mainly of water, proteins, and fat. Which colloid is more stable, milk or ice cream? How do you know?

Concentration and Solubility

 1 period, 1/2 block

ABILITY LEVELS KEY
L1 Basic to Average
L2 For All Students
L3 Average to Advanced

Objectives

7.2.1 Describe how concentration is measured.

7.2.2 Explain why solubility is useful in identifying substances.

7.2.3 Identify factors that affect the solubility of a substance.

California Standards
☐ S 8.5.d

PRETEACH

Build Background Knowledge
Students recall what they already know about concentration using a familiar example.

 Standards Warm-Up *Does It Dissolve?* **L2**

Resources

☐ **Vocabulary Flashcards**
    L2 Chapter 7 Vocabulary
☐ **Build Science Vocabulary** *Online*
    L2 Chapter 7 Vocabulary

INSTRUCT

Concentration Define and discuss concentration.

Solubility Introduce and explain solubility.

Factors Affecting Solubility Describe how solubility may be affected by pressure, type of solvent, and temperature.

Resources

☐ **Reading/Notetaking Guides**
    (Adapted versions available)
    Chapter 7, Section 2
☐ **Color Transparencies Book**
    L2 PS73
☐ **Student Edition in MP3 Format**
☐ **Spanish Section Summaries in MP3 Format**
☐ **www.SciLinks.org** Web Code: scn-1232

ASSESS/REMEDIATE

Assess Progress
Evaluate student comprehension with the Section Assessment and Section Quiz.

Remediation
Students fill in the blanks in sentences in which key terms are defined.

Resources

☐ **Teaching Resources, Unit 2**
    L2 Section 7.2 Quiz
    L1 7.2 Review and Reinforce, ELL, LPR, SN
    L3 7.2 Enrich, AR, GT

Acids, Bases, and Solutions

Acids, Bases, and Solutions • *Review and Reinforce*

Concentration and Solubility

Understanding Main Ideas

Answer the following questions on the lines below.

1. What amounts do you compare when measuring concentration?

_____

_____

2. How can you tell that a white powder is salt without tasting it?

_____

_____

3. Which solution will have more gas dissolved in it, a solution under high pressure or one under low pressure?

_____

_____

4. Explain the meaning of the expression "like dissolves like."

_____

_____

_____

5. How does temperature affect the solubility of most solids?

_____

_____

Building Vocabulary

Match each term with its definition by writing the letter of the correct definition on the line beside the term in the left column.

_____ **6.** dilute solution

_____ **7.** concentrated solution

_____ **8.** solubility

_____ **9.** saturated solution

_____ **10.** unsaturated solution

_____ **11.** supersaturated solution

a. a measure of how much solute can dissolve in a solvent at a given temperature

b. a solution that has more dissolved solute than is predicted by its solubility

c. a solution that has so much solute that no more dissolves

d. a solution that has only a little solute

e. a solution in which more solute can be dissolved

f. a solution that has a lot of solute

Temperature and Solubility

One of the factors that affects the solubility of a substance is temperature. The graph below shows how the solubilities of different solids change with the temperature of water.

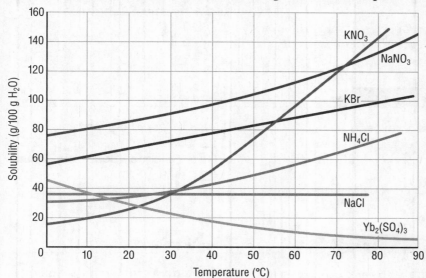

The next graph shows how the solubilities of different gases change with the temperature of water.

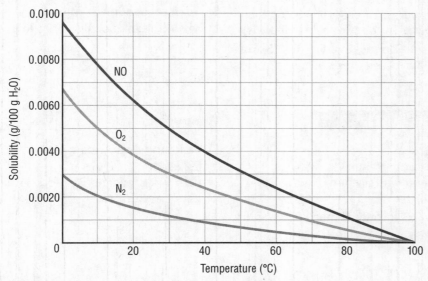

Answer the following questions on a separate sheet of paper.

1. What are the manipulated variables and the responding variables on each graph?
2. What are the general trends in solubility implied by the two graphs?
3. Do all of the solids in the first graph follow the trend? Explain.
4. Which solid shows the greatest change in solubility with temperature?
5. At higher temperatures, gas particles move faster. Use this behavior to explain the change in solubility of gases.

Describing Acids and Bases

🕑 *3 periods, 1 block*

Objectives

7.3.1 Name the properties of acids and bases.
7.3.2 Identify where acids and bases are commonly used.

🔵 California Standards

❑ S 8.5.e

PRETEACH

Build Background Knowledge

Students identify sour taste as a common property of acids in lemons and vinegar.

 **Standards Warm-Up** *What Colors Does Litmus Paper Turn?* **L2**

Resources

❑ **Vocabulary Flashcards**
  L2 Chapter 7 Vocabulary
❑ **Build Science Vocabulary** *Online*
  L2 Chapter 7 Vocabulary

INSTRUCT

Properties of Acids Introduce properties of acids, and give students examples of acids that demonstrate the properties.

Properties of Bases Guide students in inferring the properties of bases, based on the description of bases as the "opposite" of acids.

Uses of Acids and Bases Use Figures 15 and 16 to help students identify uses of specific acids and bases.

Resources

❑ **Reading/Notetaking Guides**
  (Adapted versions available)
  Chapter 7, Section 3
❑ **Student Edition in MP3 Format**
❑ **Spanish Section Summaries in MP3 Format**
❑ **www.SciLinks.org** Web Code: scn-1233

ASSESS/REMEDIATE

Assess Progress

Evaluate student comprehension with the Section Assessment and Section Quiz.

Remediation

Students help make a concept map showing the properties and uses of acids and bases.

Resources

❑ **Teaching Resources, Unit 2**
  L2 Section 7.3 Quiz
  L1 7.3 Review and Reinforce, ELL, LPR, SN
  L3 7.3 Enrich, AR, GT

Acids, Bases, and Solutions · *Review and Reinforce*

Describing Acids and Bases

Understanding Main Ideas

Complete the following table.

Characteristic	Acid	Base
When Found in Foods, What Does It Taste Like?	1.	2.
How Does It React With the Metals Magnesium, Zinc, and Iron?	3.	4.
How Does It React with Carbonates?	5.	6.
What Color Does It Turn Litmus?	7.	8.

Building Vocabulary

Answer the following questions in the spaces provided.

9. What does *corrosive* mean?

_____

_____

10. If a substance reacts with a metal to produce hydrogen gas, what may you infer about the substance?

_____

_____

11. What is an indicator?

_____

_____

12. Why do you think bases are often described as the "opposites" of acids?

_____

_____

_____

_____

Acids, Bases, and Solutions

Acids, Bases, and Solutions • *Enrich*

Acidic Paper

From the fifteenth through the eighteenth centuries, the paper in many books was made from linen. Linen is made from the fibers of flax plants. By the nineteenth century, the printing of books had increased dramatically and, as a result, so did the demand for inexpensive paper. In response, a method was developed to produce cheap paper from wood. This process involved the use of a chemical called *alum*, which greatly increased the acidity of paper. Eventually, this acidity causes such paper to become brittle and fall apart. Thus, many books made during the ninteenth and twentieth centuries are slowly becoming too fragile to read, while older books made with linen paper are often in better condition.

Scientists have developed several chemical methods to preserve books made with acidic paper. These methods involve reacting the acid in the paper with a base. The products of these reactions are not acidic, and so the paper is protected from further damage due to acidity. The diagram below illustrates one of these processes. Today, some publishers use acid-free paper in their books. In fact, important documents are sometimes printed on paper that is basic rather than acidic.

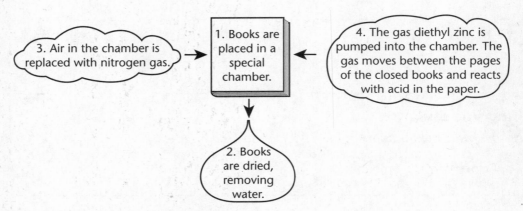

Answer the following questions on a separate sheet of paper.

1. The bases used to treat books containing acidic paper are usually gases rather than liquid solutions. Why do you think this is so?

2. Is paper made from linen more or less acidic than paper made from wood? Which type of paper lasts longer?

3. Why do you think that printing a document on basic paper will help to ensure that it lasts for a very long time?

4. How might the process of making paper from wood be changed to produce paper that is not acidic?

Acids and Bases in Solution

🕓 *4 periods, 2 blocks*

Objectives

7.4.1 State what kinds of ions acids and bases form in water.

7.4.2 Explain what pH tells you about a solution.

7.4.3 Describe what happens in a neutralization reaction.

🌐 California Standards

❏ S 8.5.e

PRETEACH

Build Background Knowledge

Students answer questions about a common acid solution as an introduction to acids and bases in solution.

 **Standards Warm-Up** *What Can Cabbage Juice Tell You?* **L2**

Resources

❏ **Vocabulary Flashcards**
   L2 Chapter 7 Vocabulary
❏ **Build Science Vocabulary** *Online*
   L2 Chapter 7 Vocabulary

INSTRUCT

Acids in Solution Guide students in understanding how acids produce ions in water.
Bases in Solution Relate the properties of bases to the ions that they produce in water.

Acid-Base Reactions Define and discuss neutralization.

 **Consumer Lab** *The Antacid Test* **L2**

Resources

❏ **Reading/Notetaking Guides**
   (Adapted versions available)
   Chapter 7, Section 4
❏ **Color Transparencies Book**
   L2 PS76, PS77, PS78, PS79
❏ **Laboratory Manual**
   L2 *The Antacid Test*
   Student Worksheets
❏ **Lab Activity DVD Library**
   L2 Skills Lab: *The Antacid Test*
❏ **Student Edition in MP3 Format**
❏ **Spanish Section Summaries in MP3 Format**
❏ **www.SciLinks.org** Web Code: cgd-2034

ASSESS/REMEDIATE

Assess Progress

Evaluate student comprehension with the Section Assessment and Section Quiz.

Remediation

Students use the key terms in sentences.

Resources

❏ **Teaching Resources, Unit 2**
   L2 Section 7.4 Quiz
   L1 7.4 Review and Reinforce, ELL, LPR, SN
   L3 7.4 Enrich, AR, GT

Acids, Bases, and Solutions

Acids and Bases in Solution

Understanding Main Ideas

Complete the concept map shown below and answer the following questions on a separate sheet of paper.

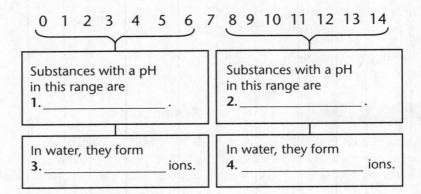

5. What is the difference between a strong acid and a weak acid?

6. What is the difference between a strong base and a weak base?

7. Which solution has a greater concentration of hydrogen ions (H^+), a solution with a pH of 3 or one with a pH of 7? Explain.

8. What are the products formed when a base reacts with an acid?

9. What is the pH of a neutral solution?

Building Vocabulary

Match each term with its definition by writing the letter of the correct symbol or definition on the line beside the term in the left column.

_____ **10.** hydroxide ion

_____ **11.** pH scale

_____ **12.** hydrogen ion

_____ **13.** neutralization

_____ **14.** salt

a. ionic compound that can form from the reaction of an acid with a base

b. reaction between an acid and a base

c. series of numbers that indicates the concentration of hydrogen ions in solution

d. H^+

e. OH^-

Name _____ Date _____ Class _____

Swimming Pool Basics

If chemicals are not added to swimming pools, tiny organisms such as bacteria and algae can multiply in the water. Algae growth can turn the water in a swimming pool cloudy and make the sides and bottom of the pool slimy. Disease-causing bacteria can make swimmers sick. One chemical added to pools contains hypochlorite ions (OCl^-). A hypochlorite ion reacts with water in the pool to produce hypochlorous acid (HOCl) and a hydroxide ion. Hypochlorous acid kills algae and bacteria. The equation for this reaction is:

$$OCl^- + H_2O \rightarrow HOCl + OH^-$$

Hypochlorite ion   Water   Hypochlorous acid   Hydroxide ion

The amount of hypochlorous acid that is produced by this reaction depends on the pH of the pool water. The ideal pH for the above reaction is 7.4. Therefore, the pH of the pool water must be carefully controlled. If the pH is too high (above 7.6), the reverse of the reaction shown above occurs:

$$HOCl + OH^- \rightarrow OCl^- + H_2O$$

Hypochlorous acid   Hydroxide ion   Hypochlorite ion   Water

As a result, there will not be enough hypochlorous acid in the pool water to control the bacteria and algae. Problems also occur when the pH of the pool water is too low (less than 7.2). Pool water having a low pH can damage the sides and bottom of the pool. Pool water having pH levels that are either too high or too low can cause eye irritation in swimmers. The graph below shows how the relative amounts of hypochlorous acid and hypochlorite ions vary with the pH of the pool water.

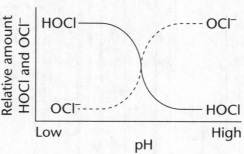

Answer the following questions on a separate sheet of paper.

1. What happens to the amount of hypochlorous acid (HOCl) in a swimming pool as the pH increases? What happens to the amount of hypochlorite ion (OCl^-)?

2. What type of chemical could you add to a swimming pool to decrease the pH of the water? Explain.

3. What type of chemical could you add to a swimming pool to increase the pH of the water? Explain.

Acids, Bases, and Solutions · *Vocabulary Skill*

Use Related Words

You can expand your vocabulary by learning the related forms of a word.
For example, the common verb to bake is related to the noun *baker* and the
adjective *baked*. As you read this chapter, look for related forms of the verbs
indicate, *saturate*, and *suspend*.

Verb	Noun	Adjective
indicate To show; to point to	**indicator** Something that shows or points to	**indicative** Serving as a sign; showing
saturate To fill up as much as is possible	**saturation** The condition of holding as much as is possible	**saturated** To be full; to hold as much as is possible
suspend To hang so as to allow free movement	**suspension** The condition of hanging or moving freely	**suspended** Hanging so as to allow free movement

Apply It!

*Review the table and complete the following sentences with the correct form of the
word. Then answer question 5.*

1. The _____ showed that the substance was an acid.

2. The problems the teacher wrote on the board was _____ of what
   would be covered on the test.

3. The _____ particles clung together in the solution.

4. The molecules fell no further, but remained in a state of
   _____.

5. Which adverb can be made by adding *-ly* to an adjective in the table?

Name _____ Date _____ Class _____

Key Terms

Match each definition in the left column with the correct term in the right column. Then write the number of each term in the appropriate box below. When you have filled in all the boxes, add up the numbers in each column, row, and two diagonals. All the sums should be the same.

A. A very well-mixed mixture

B. The part of a solution that is present in the smaller amount

C. A compound that changes color when in contact with an acid or a base

D. A substance that turns blue litmus paper red

E. A mixture that has a lot of solute dissolved in it

F. A negative ion made of oxygen and hydrogen

G. A substance that turns red litmus paper blue

H. The part of a solution that is present in the larger amount

I. Any ionic compound made from the neutralization of an acid with a base

1. solute
2. base
3. hydroxide ion (OH^-)
4. salt
5. concentrated solution
6. solution
7. acid
8. indicator
9. solvent

A. _____	B. _____	C. _____	= _____
D. _____	E. _____	F. _____	= _____
G. _____	H. _____	I. _____	= _____
= _____	= _____	= _____	= _____

Acids, Bases, and Solutions

Name _____ Date _____ Class _____

Acids, Bases, and Solutions ▪ *Pre-Assessment*

Write the letter of the correct answer on the line at the left.

_____ 1. A solution is an example of a
  a. homogeneous colloid.   **b.** heterogeneous colloid.
  c. homogeneous mixture.   **d.** heterogeneous mixture.

_____ 2. Magnesium sulfide and aluminum fluoride are
  a. ionic compounds.   **b.** molecular compounds.
  c. covalent electrons.   **d.** radioactive elements.

_____ 3. When dissolved in water, ionic compounds
  a. conduct electricity.   **b.** make the water cloudy.
  c. form double and triple   **d.** do not conduct electricity.
      bonds.

_____ 4. When dissolved in water, molecular compounds
  a. conduct electricity.   **b.** make the water cloudy.
  c. form double and triple   **d.** do not conduct electricity.
      bonds.

Name _____ Date _____ Class _____

Acids, Bases, and Solutions ▪ *Section 7.1 Quiz*

If the statement is true, write true. *If it is false, change the underlined word or words to make the statement true.*

_____ 1. Sodium chloride and other compounds are <u>solvents</u> in salt water.

_____ 2. Water <u>dissolves so many substances</u> that it is often called the "universal solvent."

_____ 3. Solutions can be formed from any combination of <u>liquids</u>.

_____ 4. Colloids and suspensions have <u>different</u> properties than solutions.

_____ 5. Salt <u>lowers the boiling point and freezing point</u> of water.

Name _____ Date _____ Class _____

Fill in the blank to complete each statement.

1. You can make a concentrated solution by adding more _____ or removing _____.

2. You can make a dilute solution by increasing the amount of _____ in a solution.

3. To measure concentration, you compare the amount of _____ to the total amount of solution.

4. You can identify a substance by its solubility because solubility is a _____ property of matter.

5. Three factors that affect the solubility of a substance are _____, _____, and _____.

Name _____ Date _____ Class _____

If the statement is true, write true. *If it is false, change the underlined word or words to make the statement true.*

_____ 1. Acids react with certain metals to produce <u>carbon dioxide</u> gas.

_____ 2. Acids react in a characteristic way with <u>cabornate</u> ions, producing carbon dioxide gas.

_____ 3. Common <u>acids</u> include sodium hydroxide, calcium hydroxide, and ammonia.

_____ 4. The reactions of the <u>base</u> baking soda with an acid, such as buttermilk, makes biscuits light and fluffy.

_____ 5. You can find acids and bases <u>exclusively in laboratories and research institutions</u>.

Acids, Bases, and Solutions

Acids, Bases, and Solutions • *Section 7.4 Quiz*

Fill in the blank to complete each statement.

1. _____ ions are the key to the reactions of acids.

2. In a solution of a _____ acid, all the acid molecules break up into ions.

3. Knowing the _____ is the key to knowing how acidic or basic a solution is.

4. The _____ expresses the concentration of hydrogen ions in a solution.

5. In a neutralization reaction, an acid reacts with a base to produce _____.

Understanding Solutions
Review and Reinforce

1. Suspension; The particles are visible and they have begun to settle out.
2. Solution; The particles are too small to see.
3. Colloid; The particles are too small to be seen, but would scatter light.
4. In an ionic solid, the positive and negative ions move apart and are surrounded by water molecules. In a molecular solid, the solid breaks into individual neutral molecules, which are surrounded by water molecules.
5. Solutes lower the freezing point and raise the boiling point of a solvent.
6. solute
7. solvent
8. colloid
9. suspension
10. solution

Understanding Solutions
Enrich

1. The water would freeze at a higher temperature than the other ingredients do. All of the water in ice cream would exist as ice. Large crystals of ice would form, which would prevent the ice cream from having a smooth texture.
2. As the particles of the colloid clump together, the air would escape from the mixture.
3. There would be no point in adding air to the mixture until the particles became sufficiently mixed and their temperature is cool enough to trap the air.
4. Milk is more stable because it remains a colloid at a much wider range of temperatures than does ice cream.

Concentration and Solubility
Review and Reinforce

1. To measure concentration, you compare the amount of solute to the amount of solvent or to the total amount of solution.
2. You could measure the solubility of the white powder in water at 0°C and compare it to a table of solubilities.
3. A solution under high pressure will have more gas dissolved in it.
4. Ionic and polar compounds usually dissolve in polar solvents. Nonpolar compounds do not usually dissolve in polar solvents.
5. For most solids, solubility increases as the temperature increases.
6. d
7. f
8. a
9. c
10. e
11. b

Concentration and Solubility
Enrich

1. For both graphs, solubility is the responding variable and temperature is the manipulated variable.
2. In general, the solubilities of solids increase with increasing temperature. The solubilities of gases decrease with increasing temperature.
3. No. $Yb_2(SO_4)_3$ is less soluble at higher temperatures. The solubility of NaCl is relatively constant.
4. The solubility of KNO_3 increases significantly between 30°C and 80°C.
5. The particles of a gas have much more energy at higher temperatures and escape from the liquid solvent more easily.

Describing Acids and Bases
Review and Reinforce

1. Sour
2. Bitter
3. Corrosive to magnesium, zinc, and iron; eats them away and produces bubbles of hydrogen gas
4. Doesn't react with metals
5. Produces carbon dioxide
6. Doesn't react with carbonates
7. Red
8. Blue
9. Corrosive describes a substance that can eat away certain materials.
10. The substance is an acid.
11. An indicator is a substance that turns different colors in an acid or a base.
12. Bases are bitter rather than sour, turn litmus paper blue rather than red, and don't react with metals or carbonates as acids do.

Describing Acids and Bases
Enrich

1. Answers may vary. Sample: Placing a book in a liquid solution would be much like soaking the book in water. The pages would become rippled, the ink might run, and the binding could be ruined.
2. Linen paper is less acidic than wood-based papers. Linen paper lasts much longer.
3. Basic paper would not become brittle and fall apart as acidic paper does. In addition, the base in the paper would react with any acid the paper might come into contact with.
4. Answers may vary. Samples: A base might be added after the stage in which alum is added, or a process for making paper without the chemical alum could be developed.

Acids and Bases in Solution
Review and Reinforce

1. acids

2. bases

3. hydrogen

4. hydroxide

5. In a strong acid, most of the molecules break up into ions in solution. In a weak acid, fewer molecules break up into ions.

6. In a strong base, most of the molecules break up into ions in solution. In a weak base, fewer molecules break up into ions.

7. The solution with a pH of 3 has a greater concentration of hydrogen ions. As pH values decrease, the concentration of hydrogen ions increases.

8. Water and a salt

9. 7

10. e

11. c

12. d

13. b

14. a

Acids and Bases in Solution
Enrich

1. As pH increases, the amount of hypochlorous acid decreases and the amount of hypochlorite ion increases.

2. An acid added to the water will decrease the pH. The acid will separate into hydrogen ions and negative ions. As the concentration of hydrogen ions increases, pH decreases.

3. A base added to the water will increase pH. The hydroxide ions in the base will react with some of the hydrogen ions in the water to produce water and a salt. This reaction will remove hydrogen ions from the water. As the concentration of hydrogen ions decreases, pH increases.

Vocabulary Skill

1. indicator
2. indicative
3. suspended
4. suspension
5. indicatively

Key Terms

A. 6
B. 1
C. 8
D. 7
E. 5
F. 3
G. 2
H. 9
I. 4

Sums: 15

Pre-Assessment

1. C
2. A
3. A
4. D

Section 7.1 Quiz

1. solutes
2. true
3. solids, liquids, and gases
4. true
5. raises the boiling point and lowers the freezing point

Section 7.2 Quiz

1. solute; solvent
2. solvent
3. solute
4. characteristic
5. pressure; type of solvent; temperature

Section 7.3 Quiz

1. hydrogen
2. true
3. bases
4. true
5. almost anywhere

Section 7.4 Quiz

1. Hydrogen
2. strong
3. concentration of hydrogen ions
4. pH scale
5. salt and water

Chapter 8 Carbon Chemistry

Properties of Carbon

🕐 *1 period, 1/2 block*

Objectives

8.1.1　Explain why carbon plays a central role in the chemistry of living organisms.

8.1.2　Identify four forms of pure carbon

🌐 **California Standards**
❏ S 8.6.a

PRETEACH

Build Background Knowledge
Students explain why they think people value diamonds.

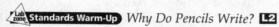 **Standards Warm-Up** *Why Do Pencils Write?* **L2**

Resources

❏ **Vocabulary Flashcards**
　　L2 Chapter 8 Vocabulary
❏ **Build Science Vocabulary** *Online*
　　L2 Chapter 8 Vocabulary

INSTRUCT

Carbon Atoms and Bonding Use dot diagrams and structural diagrams to lead a discussion describing how carbon bonds to itself and to other elements.

Forms of Pure Carbon Ask questions to lead the class in completing a compare/contrast table of the forms of pure carbon.

Resources

❏ **Reading/Notetaking Guides**
　　(Adapted versions available)
　　Chapter 8, Section 1
❏ **Color Transparencies Book**
　　L2 PS84, PS85
❏ **Student Edition in MP3 Format**
❏ **Spanish Section Summaries in MP3 Format**
❏ **www.SciLinks.org** Web Code: cgp-2041

ASSESS/REMEDIATE

Assess Progress
Evaluate student comprehension with the Section Assessment and Section Quiz.

Remediation
Students diagram how carbon atoms form bonds with other carbon atoms.

Resources

❏ **Teaching Resources, Unit 2**
　　L2 Section 8.1 Quiz
　　L1 8.1 Review and Reinforce, ELL, LPR, SN
　　L3 8.1 Enrich, AR, GT

Properties of Carbon

Understanding Main Ideas

For items 1–4 below, correctly label each structure as one of the forms of elemental carbon.

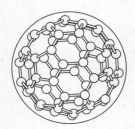 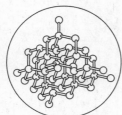 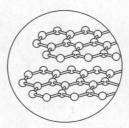 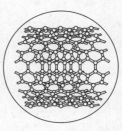

1. _____ 2. _____ 3. _____ 4. _____

Fill in the blank with the word or words that best completes each sentence.

5. Each carbon atom has _____ valence electrons for forming bonds.

6. Carbon atoms can bond with other _____ and with atoms of other elements in many different ways.

Building Vocabulary

Answer the following questions in the spaces provided.

7. Which form of carbon in the figure above is the hardest?

_____

8. Which form of carbon in the figure above feels slippery?

_____

9. Which form of carbon in the figure above may possibly be used to carry other substances inside the molecule?

_____

10. Which form of carbon in the figure above is also good a conductor of electricity and heat?

_____

Carbon Chemistry · *Enrich*

Charcoal

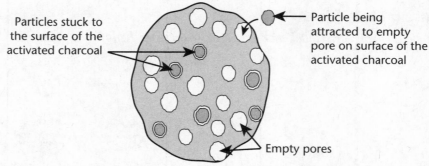

Particles stuck to the surface of the activated charcoal

Particle being attracted to empty pore on surface of the activated charcoal

Empty pores

Grain of Activated Charcoal

If you've ever built a campfire or a fire in a fireplace, you know what is left after the fire goes out—charcoal. Charcoal is the black material formed when wood is burned. It is actually an impure form of graphite. Charcoal has lots of very small openings, or pores, throughout its structure. Another form of charcoal, called activated charcoal, is made by burning wood at very high temperatures with very little air. This process produces an even greater number of these extremely small pores throughout the charcoal.

Because of the tiny pores throughout the material, charcoal and activated charcoal are very useful. These openings can attract molecules and make them stick to their surfaces as shown in the figure above.

Activated charcoal can be used to remove harmful chemicals and bacteria from drinking water. It is also used in aquarium filters to keep the water in the tank clean. As the water flows through the pores in the activated charcoal, some of the substances in the water, such as pesticides, bacteria, and particles, are attracted to the surfaces of the pores. These materials then stick to the charcoal and are removed from the water.

Answer the following on a separate sheet of paper.

1. Another use for activated charcoal is in treating people and animals who have swallowed poisonous substances. How do you think activated charcoal removes a poison from a person's or an animal's body?

2. As well as removing particles from water and other liquids, activated charcoal can also remove particles from the air. Give examples of how activated charcoal might be used in this way.

3. Some backpackers carry a special kind of straw with them that contains a small filter made of activated charcoal. The straw is for use when clean drinking water is not available. How can the special straw be used to obtain clean drinking water?

4. Bacteria that is removed from drinking water by activated charcoal remains stuck to the surface of the charcoal. If the same activated charcoal is used for a long period of time to remove bacteria, a quantity of bacteria can build up on it. Manufacturers of drinking water filters made of activated charcoal recommend that the filter material be changed at least once a year. Why do you think this is a good idea?

Carbon Compounds

4 periods, 2 blocks

Objectives

.2.1 Identify some properties of organic compounds.

.2.2 Identify some properties of hydrocarbons.

.2.3 Describe the structure and bonding of hydrocarbons.

.2.4 List characteristics of substituted hydrocarbons, esters, and polymers.

California Standards

❏ S 8.3.c
❏ S 8.6.a

PRETEACH

Build Background Knowledge
Students describe properties of gasoline that they have observed.

Standards Warm-Up *What Do You Smell?* **L2**

Resources

❏ **Vocabulary Flashcards**
   L2 Chapter 8 Vocabulary
❏ **Build Science Vocabulary** *Online*
   L2 Chapter 8 Vocabulary

INSTRUCT

Organic Compounds Use the definition of *organic compound* in a discussion of their properties.

Hydrocarbons Use structural formulas of different hydrocarbons to discuss different ways that carbon can form bonds.

Structure of Hydrocarbons Use structural formulas of different hydrocarbons to discuss different ways that carbon can form bonds

Substituted Hydrocarbons Use structural formulas of methanol and formic acid in a discussion about substituted hydrocarbons.

Esters Lead a discussion about the characteristics of esters.

Polymers Model monomers and polymers to illustrate what polymers are and how they form.

Skills Lab *How Many Molecules?* **L2**

Resources

❏ **Reading/Notetaking Guides**
   (Adapted versions available)
   Chapter 8, Section 2
❏ **Color Transparencies Book**
   L2 PS87, PS88, PS89, PS90
❏ **Laboratory Manual**
   L2 *How Many Molecules?*
   Student Worksheets
❏ **Lab Activity DVD Library**
   L2 Skills Lab: *How Many Molecules?*
❏ **Student Edition in MP3 Format**
❏ **Spanish Section Summaries in MP3 Format**
❏ **www.SciLinks.org** Web Code: scn-1242

ASSESS/REMEDIATE

Assess Progress
Evaluate student comprehension with the Section Assessment and Section Quiz.

Remediation
Students relate hydrocarbons, substituted hydrocarbons, esters, and polymers in a concept map.

Resources

❏ **Teaching Resources, Unit 2**
   L2 Section 8.2 Quiz
   L1 8.2 Review and Reinforce, ELL, LPR, SN
   L3 8.2 Enrich, AR, GT

Carbon Chemistry

Carbon Chemistry · *Review and Reinforce*

Carbon Compounds

Understanding Main Ideas

Answer the following questions on a separate sheet of paper.

1. What kinds of carbon chains are shown in Figures 1 through 3?

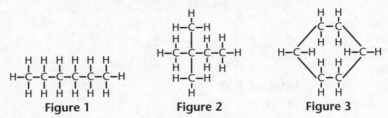

Figure 1   Figure 2   Figure 3

2. Write the chemical formulas for the three compounds shown above.

3. The compounds in Figure 1 and Figure 2 have the same number of carbon and hydrogen atoms. This fact makes them what type of compounds?

Building Vocabulary

Match each term with its definition by writing the letter of the correct definition in the right column on the line beside the term in the left column.

____ 4. substituted hydrocarbon	a. a compound that contains carbon
____ 5. organic compound	b. —OH
____ 6. ester	c. very large molecule made of many smaller molecules bonded together
____ 7. polymer	d. a substituted hydrocarbon with one or more hydroxyl groups
____ 8. hydroxyl group	
____ 9. structural formula	e. a compound containing only the elements carbon and hydrogen
____ 10. hydrocarbon	f. —COOH
____ 11. alcohol	g. a molecule with an atom of another element in place of hydrogen
____ 12. carboxyl group	
____ 13. monomer	h. the compound that results when an alcohol and an organic acid are chemically combined
____ 14. organic acid	
	i. shows the kind, number, and arrangement of atoms of a molecule
	j. the smaller molecules that make up a polymer
	k. a substituted hydrocarbon with one or more carboxyl groups

Simplest Hydrocarbons

The simplest hydrocarbons belong to a family called alkanes. The alkane family is made up of compounds that contain only carbon and hydrogen atoms. The carbon atoms in an alkane are connected to one another by single bonds only. The table below shows the first ten alkanes, their formulas, their states at room temperature, and their melting and boiling points. The carbon atoms in each compound form a straight chain.

Name	Formula	State at Room Temperature	Melting Point (©C)	Boiling Point (©C)
Methane	CH_4	gas	−184	−161.4
Ethane	C_2H_6	gas	−172	−88.3
Propane	C_3H_8	gas	−189.9	−44.5
Butane	C_4H_{10}	gas	−135	−0.55
Pentane	C_5H_{12}	liquid	−131.5	36.2
Hexane	C_6H_{14}	liquid	−94.3	69
Heptane	C_7H_{16}	liquid	−90	98.4
Octane	C_8H_{18}	liquid	−56.5	124.6
Nonane	C_9H_{20}	liquid	−51	150.6
Decane	$C_{10}H_{22}$	liquid	−32	174

Answer the following questions on a separate sheet of paper.

1. As the number of carbon atoms in the compound increases, what pattern do you see in the boiling points? What general pattern do you see in the melting points?
2. The alkane with a formula of $C_{14}H_{30}$ is a liquid at room temperature. Predict the state of the compound $C_{12}H_{26}$ at room temperature. Explain your reasoning.
3. There is a relationship between the number of hydrogen atoms and the number of carbon atoms in an alkane. This relationship does not change, no matter how many carbon atoms an alkane contains. Describe that relationship in a statement or as a mathematical formula.
4. Based on the table and your answer to item 3, what is the chemical formula of the alkane that contains 40 carbon atoms?

Carbon Chemistry

Polymers and Composites

🕐 *1 period, 1/2 block*

Objectives
8.3.1   Explain how polymers form.
8.3.2   Tell what composites are made of.
8.3.3   Explain how to help reduce the amount of plastic waste.

🌐 California Standards
❑ S 8.3.c
❑ S 8.6.a

PRETEACH

Build Background Knowledge
Students identify items made of plastic.

 **Standards Warm-Up** *What Did You Make?* **L2**

Resources

❑ **Vocabulary Flashcards**
   L2 Chapter 8 Vocabulary
❑ **Build Science Vocabulary** *Online*
   L2 Chapter 8 Vocabulary

INSTRUCT

Forming Polymers Use simple chemical formulas of proteins and sugars to explain how polymers form.
Polymers and Composites Lead a discussion about composites and how they relate to polymers.
Recycling Plastics Use a chart to organize the benefits and problems of polymers.

Resources

❑ **Reading/Notetaking Guides**
   (Adapted versions available)
   Chapter 8, Section 3
❑ **Color Transparencies Book**
   L2 PS93
❑ **Student Edition in MP3 Format**
❑ **Spanish Section Summaries in MP3 Format**
❑ **www.SciLinks.org** Web Code: cgd-1041

ASSESS/REMEDIATE

Assess Progress
Evaluate student comprehension with the Section Assessment and Section Quiz.

Remediation
Students make a concept map that relates monomers, polymers, and composites.

Resources

❑ **Teaching Resources, Unit 2**
   L2 Section 8.3 Quiz
   L1 8.3 Review and Reinforce, ELL, LPR, SN
   L3 8.3 Enrich, AR, GT

Name _____ Date_____ Class _____

Polymers and Composites

Understanding Main Ideas

Use the diagram below to answer questions 1–3.

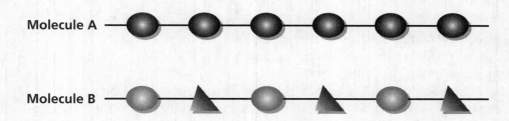

Molecule A

Molecule B

1. What type of molecules are modeled by the diagram?
   _____

2. What do the ovals and triangles represent? _____

3. In what way does Molecule A differ from Molecule B?
   _____

Answer the following questions in the spaces provided.

4. Describe how polymers form.
   _____

5. What are composites made of? Give an example.
   _____
   _____

Label each of the following as a benefit or a disadvantage related to the use of synthetic polymers.

6. strong _____
7. increase the volume of trash _____
8. may last thousands of years _____
9. inexpensive to make _____

Building Vocabulary

Match each term with its definition by writing the letter of the correct definition in the right column on the line beside the term in the left column.

____ 10. protein

____ 11. amino acid

____ 12. plastic

____ 13. composite

a. two or more substances combined as a new material with different properties

b. a type of polymer found in living things

c. small molecules that join to form proteins

d. a synthetic polymer that can be molded or shaped

Carbon Chemistry • *Enrich*

Degradable Plastics

You learned that one solution to the disposal problem of plastics is recycling. Another possible solution to this problem is the use of degradable plastics. *Degradable plastics* are designed to break down in the environment much more quickly than regular plastics. There are two main types of degradable plastics: photodegradable (*photo-* means light) and biodegradable (*bio-* means life).

Photodegradable plastics break down into smaller pieces after being exposed to a certain amount of sunlight. *Biodegradable* plastics contain a natural polymer in addition to synthetic polymers. The most common natural polymer added to biodegradable plastics is cornstarch. Cornstarch is a polymer of sugar molecules that can be decomposed by microorganisms such as bacteria. When this happens, the plastic breaks down into smaller pieces.

One area in which degradable plastics are being used today involves erosion control. In places where land has been cleared, such as during highway construction, erosion control blankets made with layers of degradable plastic and straw can be placed on the soil. The blanket keeps the soil from being washed away until new plants have a chance to grow. Once the blanket has broken down, the plants' roots will be able to keep the soil in place.

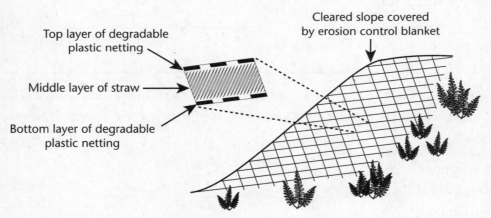

Top layer of degradable plastic netting

Middle layer of straw

Bottom layer of degradable plastic netting

Cleared slope covered by erosion control blanket

Answer the following questions on a separate sheet of paper.

1. Do you think photodegradable plastic that is buried in a landfill will break down quickly? Explain.

2. Most landfills contain very little air and moisture, which many bacteria need to survive. How do you think these conditions affect biodegradable plastic buried in a landfill?

3. Why do you think it is important that an erosion control blanket break down after a few weeks or months?

4. Name two other everyday objects that you think should be made out of degradable plastic.

Life With Carbon

2 1/2 periods, 1 1/3 blocks

ABILITY LEVELS KEY
L1 Basic to Average
L2 For All Students
L3 Average to Advanced

Objectives

8.4.1 List the four main classes of organic compounds required by living things.
8.4.2 Explain why living things need water, vitamins, minerals, and salts.

California Standards
❑ S 8.6.b
❑ S 8.6.c

PRETEACH

Build Background Knowledge
Students discuss what various foods have in common in order to understand the role of carbon in the chemistry of living things.

 **Standards Warm-Up** *What Is in Milk?* **L2**

Resources
❑ **Vocabulary Flashcards**
   L2 Chapter 8 Vocabulary
❑ **Build Science Vocabulary** *Online*
   L2 Chapter 8 Vocabulary

INSTRUCT

Carbohydrates Lead a discussion in which students compare and contrast simple and complex carbohydrates.
Proteins Use the structural formulas of alanine and serine to discuss protein structure.
Lipids Ask questions in a discussion about lipids contrasted with carbohydrates.
Nucleic Acids Lead a discussion about the structure of nucleic acids and their importance to living things.
Other Nutrients Ask questions in a discussion about vitamins and minerals.

 **Consumer Lab** *Are You Getting Your Vitamins?* **L2**

Resources
❑ **Reading/Notetaking Guides**
   (Adapted versions available)
   Chapter 8, Section 4
❑ **Color Transparencies Book**
   L2 PS95, PS96
❑ **Laboratory Manual**
   L2 *Are You Getting Your Vitamins?*
   Student Worksheets
❑ **Lab Activity DVD Library**
   L2 Skills Lab: *Are You Getting Your Vitamins?*
❑ **Student Edition in MP3 Format**
❑ **Spanish Section Summaries in MP3 Format**
❑ **www.SciLinks.org** Web Code: scn-1243

ASSESS/REMEDIATE

Assess Progress
Evaluate student comprehension with the Section Assessment and Section Quiz.

Remediation
Students relate the key terms in a concept map.

Resources
❑ **Teaching Resources, Unit 2**
   L2 Section 8.4 Quiz
   L1 8.4 Review and Reinforce, ELL, LPR, SN
   L3 8.4 Enrich, AR, GT

Carbon Chemistry

Carbon Chemistry • *Review and Reinforce*

Life With Carbon

Understanding Main Ideas

Answer the following questions on a separate sheet of paper.

1. What are the four main classes of organic compounds in living things?
2. Why are starch and cellulose considered different compounds even though they are both built from glucose?
3. How does DNA determine the differences among living things?
4. Describe your body's requirements for vitamins and minerals.

Building Vocabulary

Fill in the blank with the word or words that best completes each sentence.

glucose	carbohydrate	amino acids	DNA
cellulose	proteins	cholesterol	lipids
nucleic acid	fatty acids	nucleotide	
complex carbohydrate	starch	RNA	

5. Twenty different _____ make up proteins.

6. Each lipid molecule is composed of three _____ and one alcohol.

7. Different _____ are made when different sequences of amino acids are linked into long chains.

8. Gram for gram, _____ release twice as much energy in your body as do _____.

9. A very large organic compound made up of carbon, oxygen, hydrogen, nitrogen, and phosphorus is called a(n) _____.

10. _____ and _____ are the two types of nucleic acids.

11. The monomer that makes up a nucleic acid is a(n) _____.

12. A long chain of energy-rich organic compounds made of glucose molecules is called a(n) _____

13. _____ is a waxy substance found in all animal cells.

14. _____ is a simple carbohydrate. Both _____ and _____ are complex carbohydrates.

Carbon Chemistry · *Enrich*

Protein Structures

The bodies of all mammals, such as humans, cows, sheep, whales, and horses, contain similar but not identical proteins. One of these proteins is called *insulin*. Insulin helps to regulate the concentration of sugar in a mammal's blood. What makes one mammal's insulin different from another is the sequence of amino acids within the molecule. Each mammal listed in the table below has 51 amino acids in its insulin molecule. Most of the molecule is the same for all of these mammals. However, one portion of the molecule is different. The table shows that portion, and the sequence in which the different amino acids combine. The full names of the amino acids are abbreviated in the table as follows: cys (cysteine); ala (alanine); ser (serine); val (valine); thr (threonine); ile (isoleucine); and gly (glycine).

Mammal	Amino Acid Sequence
cows	-cys-ala-ser-val-cys-
whale	-cys-thr-ser-ile-cys-
sheep	-cys-ala-gly-val-cys-
horse	-cys-thr-gly-ile-cys-
human	-cys-thr-ser-ile-cys-

Answer the following questions on a separate sheet of paper.

1. Which two insulin molecules are most alike?
2. Based on the table, how does the sequence of amino acids in horse insulin differ from the sequence in whale insulin?
3. Scientists think that the structure of proteins may reveal how closely related different animals are. Based on this assumption, which are more closely related: horses and cows or sheep and cows? Explain your answer.
4. The first medical treatment for diabetes, a disease in which the body lacks insulin, was to provide insulin from another animal. Based on the information above, suggest a hypothesis to explain why such treatment could work.

Carbon Chemistry

Carbon Chemistry ▪ *Vocabulary Skill*

Use Clues to Determine Meaning

Science textbooks often contain unfamiliar words. When you are reading, use clues to figure out what these words mean. First, look for clues in the word itself. Then look at the surrounding words, sentences, and paragraph. Look at the clues to determine the meaning of *nanotube* in the following paragraph.

   In 1991, scientists made another form of carbon—the <u>nanotube</u>. A **nanotube** is a <u>form of carbon in which atoms are arranged in the shape of a long, hollow cylinder or tube</u>. Only a <u>few nanometers wide in diameter</u>, nanotubes are <u>tiny, light, flexible, and extremely strong</u>. They also are <u>good conductors of electricity and heat</u>.

Apply It!

Answer the questions based on the paragraph above.

1. What piece of additional information is contained in the first sentence?
2. If you didn't know the meaning of **nanometers** what context clues in the third sentence might help you determine its meaning?
3. What are nanotubes good conductors of?
4. If the definition were not included in the paragraph, what clue in the word itself might help you figure out its meaning?

Name _____ Date _____ Class _____

Key Terms

Use the clues below to identify Key Terms from the chapter. Write the terms on the lines, putting one letter in each blank. When you finish, the word enclosed in the diagonal will reveal an important term related to the chemistry of living things. Define the term.

Clues

1. A form of pure carbon with atoms arranged in the shape of a long, hollow tube.
2. A form of pure carbon with atoms arranged in the shape of a hollow sphere.
3. A substituted hydrocarbon that contains one or more hydroxyl groups
4. A simple sugar found in the body
5. A complex carbohydrate that strengthens plant stems and roots
6. The —COOH part in a molecule of an organic acid
7. A formula that shows the kind, number, and arrangement of atoms in a molecule
8. The monomers in a protein molecule
9. A compound that contains only the elements carbon and hydrogen
10. An organic compound made by chemically combining an alcohol and an organic acid

1. __ __ __ __ __ __ __ __

2. __ __ __ __ __ __ __ __ __ __

3. __ __ __ __ __ __

4. __ __ __ __ __ __ __

5. __ __ __ __ __ __ __ __ __

6. __ __ __ __ __ __ __ __ __ __

7. __ __ __ __ __ __ __ __ __ __ __ __

8. __ __ __ __ __ __ __ __ __ __ __

9. __ __ __ __ __ __ __ __ __ __

10. __ __ __ __ __ __

Hidden Term: _____

Definition: _____

_____

Name _____ Date _____ Class _____

Carbon Chemistry · *Pre-Assessment*

Write the letter of the correct answer on the line at the left.

_____ 1. A chemical bond is
   a. a way of organizing elements in the periodic table.
   b. the force that holds two atoms together.
   c. how elements react with each other.
   d. a result of combustion.

_____ 2. The ways in which an atom can bond with other atoms depends on the atom's
   a. valence electrons.   b. nucleus.
   c. atomic number.   d. atomic mass.

_____ 3. In a carbon dioxide molecule (CO_2), carbon forms a(n)
   a. ionic compound with oxygen.
   b. atomic number.
   c. polyatomic ion.
   d. double bond with each of two oxygen atoms.

_____ 4. The most loosely held electrons in an atom are
   a. unstable electrons.   b. covalent electrons.
   c. valence electrons.   d. low-energy electrons.

Name _____ Date _____ Class _____

Carbon Chemistry · *Section 8.1 Quiz*

If the statement is true, write true. *If it is false, change the underlined word or words to make the statement true.*

_____ 1. Two forms of pure carbon are <u>gold</u> and graphite.

_____ 2. Carbon is <u>similar to other</u> elements because it can bond to itself and to many other elements.

_____ 3. Carbon can form four bonds because it has four <u>valence electrons</u>.

_____ 4. Carbon atoms can be arranged in straight chains, branched chains, and <u>helixes</u>.

_____ 5. In a <u>fullerene</u>, carbon atoms are arranged in the shape of a long, hollow cylinder.

Carbon Chemistry · *Section 8.2 Quiz*

Fill in the blank to complete each statement.

1. _____ can be found in living things, products made from living things, and materials produced artificially in laboratories and factories.

2. Four common properties of organic compounds are _____ melting points, _____ boiling points, _____ electrical conductivity, and _____ solubility in water.

3. Hydrocarbons can be classified by the arrangements of their atoms and by the types of _____between carbon atoms.

4. Butane and isobutane are _____ with different structural formulas, melting points, and boiling points.

5. If _____ of another element is substituted for a hydrogen atom in a hydrocarbon, a different compound is created.

Carbon Chemistry · *Section 8.3 Quiz*

If the statement is true, write true. *If it is false, change the underlined word or words to make the statement true.*

_____   1. Food, materials, living things, and plastic are all made of <u>organic</u> compounds.

_____   2. <u>Oxygen</u> is the most common element found in compounds with carbon.

_____   3. The properties of a protein depend on which <u>esters</u> are used to form the polymer and in what order.

_____   4. The starting materials for many synthetic polymers come from coal or <u>natural gas</u>.

_____   5. Fiberglass is a type of <u>monomer</u>.

Carbon Chemistry · *Section 8.4 Quiz*

Fill in the blank to complete each statement.

1. Living things require four classes of organic compounds: _____, _____, _____, and _____.

2. _____ are the simplest carbohydrates.

3. Starch and cellulose are two _____ assembled from glucose.

4. A bird's feathers, a fish's scales, and your fingernails are all made of _____.

5. To help support the function of large molecules, organisms require simple substances such as _____, _____, _____, and _____.

Properties of Carbon
Review and Reinforce
1. fullerene
2. diamond
3. graphite
4. nanotube
5. four
6. carbon atoms
7. diamond
8. graphite
9. fullerene
10. nanotube

Properties of Carbon
Enrich
1. The tiny pores in the activated charcoal will attract the molecules of poison and make them stick to the charcoal's surface. The poison molecules will then be passed out of the human or animal's body along with the activated charcoal.
2. Answers will vary. Sample: Activated charcoal can be used to filter out particles of pollution from air. It can also be used in gas masks to remove certain poisonous gas particles.
3. The backpacker can sip water from streams, lakes, and rivers through the special straw. The activated charcoal in the straw will attract and remove most bacteria from the water.
4. Answers may vary. Sample: A buildup of bacteria will eventually prevent the charcoal from attracting bacteria to its surface. This will cause the activated charcoal to stop working. Also, a layer of dead bacteria is a good place for live bacteria to grow and multiply. This would contaminate the water.

Carbon Compounds
Review and Reinforce
1. Figure 1: a straight chain
   Figure 2: a branched chain
   Figure 3: a ring-shaped chain
2. C_6H_{14}, C_6H_{14}, C_6H_{12}
3. isomers
4. g
5. a
6. h
7. c
8. b
9. i
10. e
11. d
12. f
13. j
14. k

Carbon Compounds
Enrich
1. As the number of carbon atoms in the alkane increases, the boiling point of the compound increases. The pattern for the melting points is the same, with the exception of propane.
2. Liquid; melting points generally increase as the number of carbon atoms increases, and the melting points of $C_{10}H_{22}$ and $C_{14}H_{30}$ make them both liquids at room temperature. The melting point of any alkane between $C_{10}H_{22}$ and $C_{14}H_{30}$ should also make it a liquid.
3. The number of hydrogen atoms in an alkane equals twice the number of carbon atoms plus 2; C_nH_{2n+2}, or a similar expression is acceptable.
4. $C_{40}H_{82}$

Polymers and Composites
Review and Reinforce
1. polymers
2. different kinds of monomers
3. Molecule A is made of one kind of monomer while Molecule B is made of two kinds of monomers in an alternating pattern. (Some students may also note that the monomers in the two molecules are different.)
4. Polymers form when chemical bonds link large numbers of monomers in a repeating pattern.
5. Two or more substances, often including one or more polymers; Samples: wood or fiberglass
6. benefit
7. disadvantage
8. may be a benefit or a disadvantage
9. benefit
10. b
11. c
12. d
13. a

Polymers and Composites
Enrich
1. No. The plastic must be exposed to sunlight in order to break down quickly. If it is buried, no sunlight will reach it.
2. With little air and moisture, bacteria that can break down the biodegradable plastics cannot live. The plastics will not break down very quickly and the volume of plastic trash will increase.

3. Answers may vary. Sample: If an erosion control blanket did not break down, there would be a netting of plastic on the ground that would last for a very long time. This netting could be dangerous to animals if they became tangled in it.

4. Answers will vary. Sample: plastic grocery bags and plastic cups

Life With Carbon
Review and Reinforce

1. The four main classes of organic compounds in living things are carbohydrates, proteins, lipids, and nucleic acids.

2. Starch and cellulose are considered different compounds because their glucose molecules are arranged differently.

3. The differences among living things depend on the order of nucleotides in their DNA.

4. The body needs vitamins and minerals only in small amounts for chemical reactions and body processes.

5. amino acids
6. fatty acids
7. proteins
8. lipids; carbohydrates
9. nucleic acid
10. DNA; RNA
11. nucleotide
12. complex carbohydrate
13. cholesterol
14. glucose; starch; cellulose

Life With Carbon
Enrich

1. Whale and human; they are identical.
2. The sequences differ in the third amino acid.
3. Sheep and cows; there is only one difference in the structure of their insulin molecules, there are three differences between horses and cows.
4. Insulin from another animal is enough like human insulin that it worked the same way.

Vocabulary Skill

1. Nanotubes were first made by scientists in 1991.
2. Sample: The words "few" and "tiny" indicate that a *nanometer* is a very small measurement of distance.
3. They are good for conducting electricity and heat.

4. The word "tube" contained in nanotube would be a clue to what it is.

Key Terms

1. nanotube
2. fullerene
3. alcohol
4. glucose
5. cellulose
6. carboxyl group
7. structural formula
8. amino acids
9. hydrocarbon
10. ester
   Hidden term: nucleotide
   Definition: A nucleotide is the building block of nucleic acids.

Pre-Assessment

1. B
2. A
3. D
4. C

Section 8.1 Quiz

1. Sample answers: diamond, fullerenes, nanotubes
2. unique among the
3. true
4. rings
5. nanotube

Section 8.2 Quiz

1. Organic compounds
2. low; low; poor; low
3. bonds
4. isomers
5. one atom

Section 8.3 Quiz

1. true
2. Hydrogen
3. amino acids
4. oil
5. composite

Section 8.4 Quiz

1. proteins; lipids; carbohydrates; nucleic acids
2. Sugars
3. complex carbohydrates
4. proteins
5. vitamins; water; minerals; salts